National
Folk
Museum of
Korea

Notice

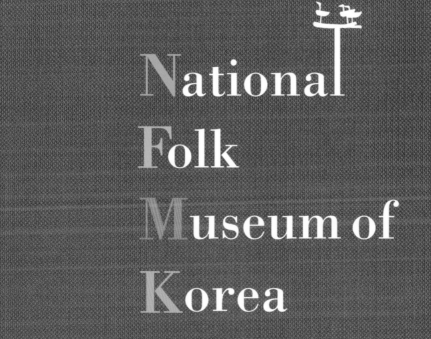

National
Folk
Museum of
Korea

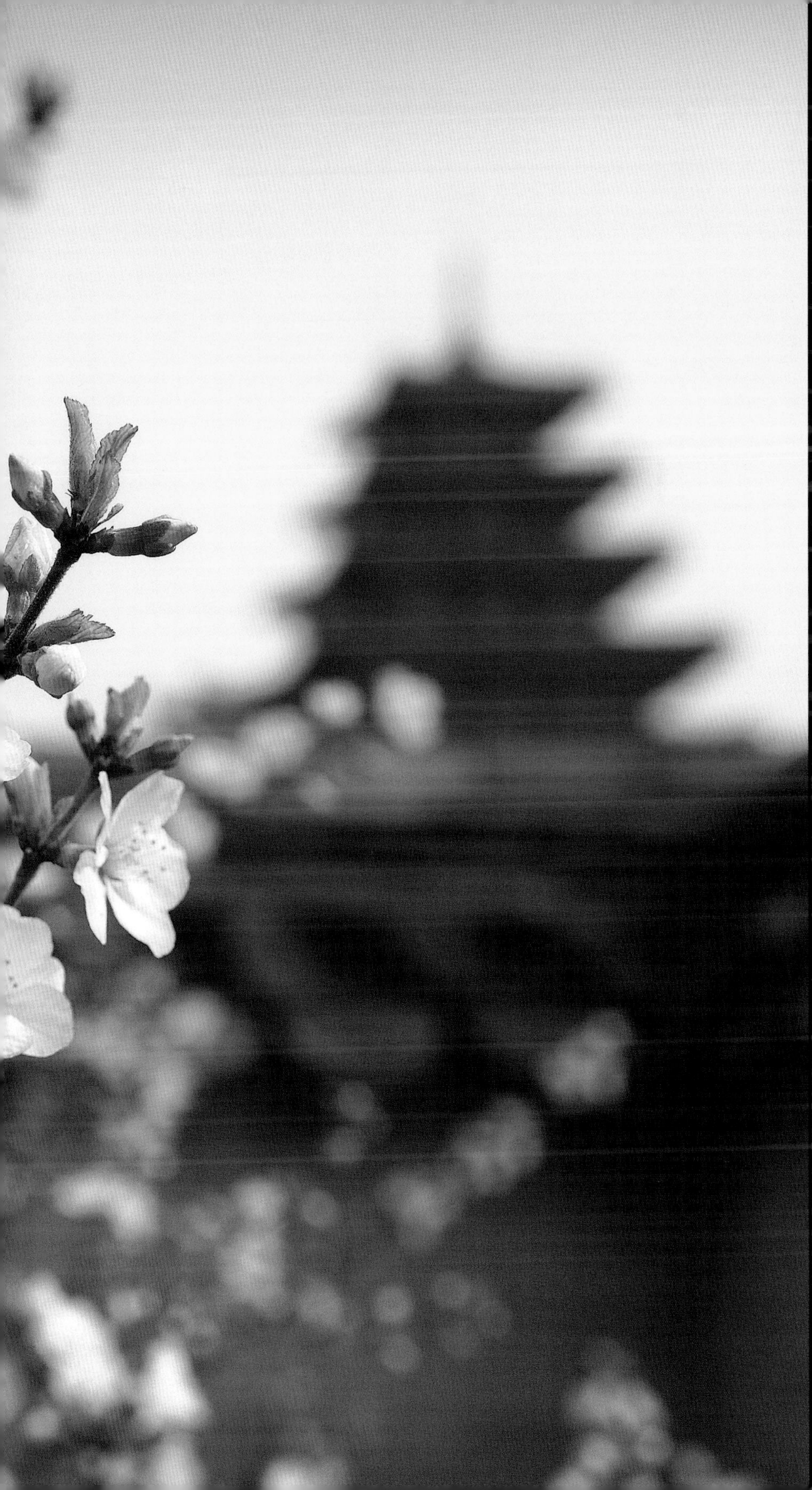

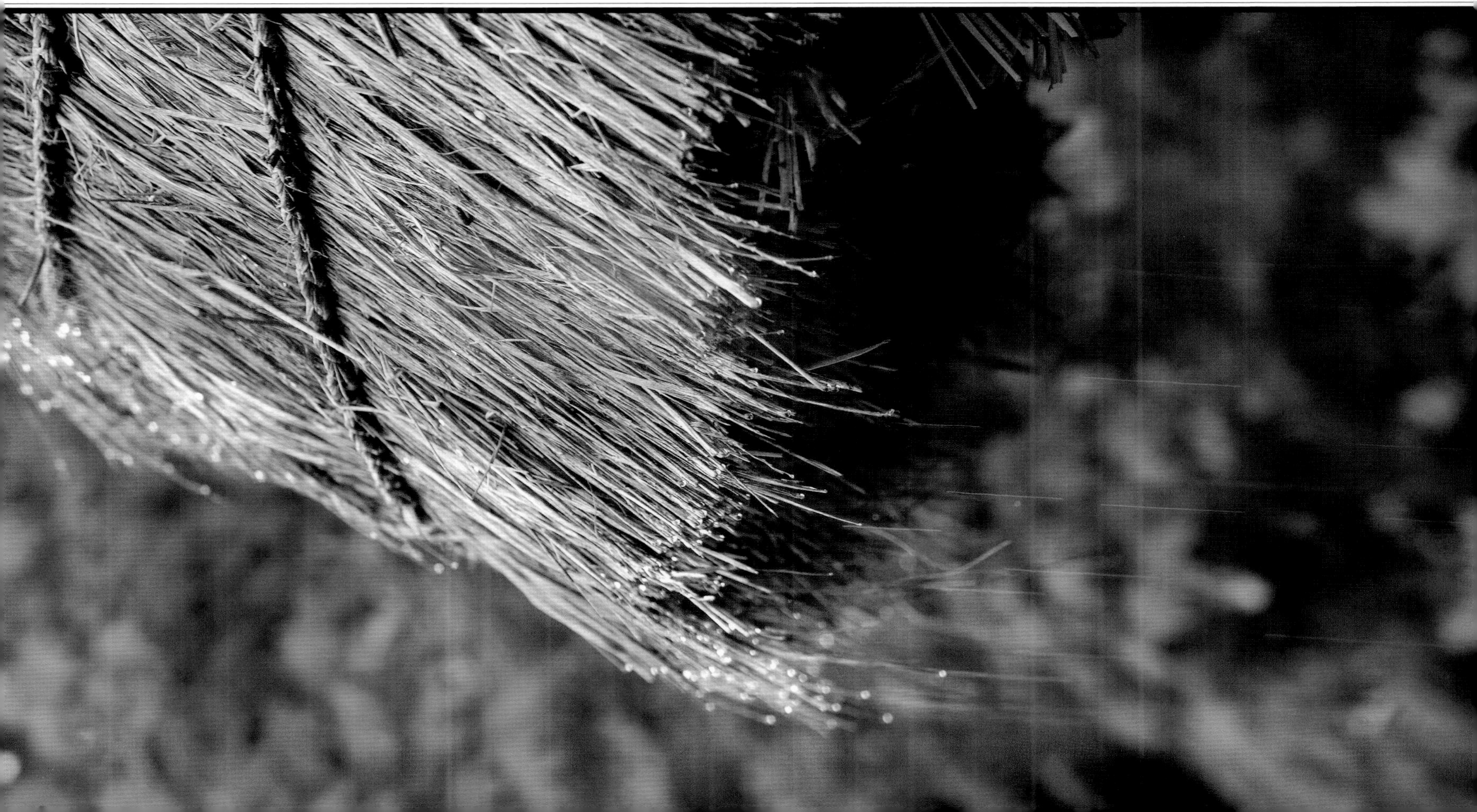

Introduction

It has been 60 years since The National Folk Museum of Korea was established. The museum has gone though many changes in its history. Its name and location changed four times while the themes of the exhibitions varied in each of its transition periods.

However there has been one constant during all the changes: the determination to feature the daily lives and stories of the people who lived through this course of history. The museum has made extraordinary efforts to collect ordinary items and other historical material from different eras in order to offer visitors vivid representations of each period.

The dramatic changes in modern lifestyles mean that museums are required to change and improve their exhibitions with a more contemporary touch. The National Folk Museum utilizes a broad range of videos and the latest technology to narrow the distance between the relics of the past and the expectations of visitors from the digital age. The museum has also recreated the streets of the 1960s and 1970s inside its halls to give visitors a truer sense of those times, rather than just relying on the items on display behind glass.

Now The National Folk Museum seeks to become a place where visitors can journey through history as well as providing them with a comfortable urban retreat from their bustling daily lives. We hope that more people will be able to enjoy and experience Korea's traditional way of life and folk culture in order to better understand how deeply rooted these elements are in the lives of Korea's present inhabitants.

Thank you.

Director, The National Folk Museum of Korea

Contents

The Korean Way of Life — 86

Korean Life Passages — 214

A Street to the Past — 320

How The National Folk Museum of Korea Came to Be Built

The story of The National Folk Museum building is connected to the history of the museum itself. For most of its first 50 years of existence, the museum moved around buildings built during the Joseon Kingdom and the Japanese colonial period. When the museum was established in 1946, then as The National Museum of Ethnology, it used the *Namsan* Civic Memorial Hall in downtown Seoul. The museum then was housed in Sujeongjeon Hall of *Gyeongbok* Palace between 1966 and 1975, when it was known as The Korean Folk Hall under the Office of Cultural Properties. In 1975, the museum, then renamed The Korean Folk Museum, moved to the old Japanese Government-General Building in the *Gyeongbok* Palace grounds and stayed there until 1992, a year

The Korean Folk Hall, 1966(*Gyeongbok* Palace, *Sujeongjeon*)

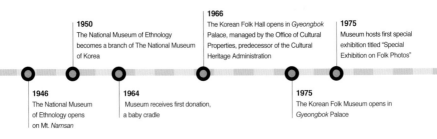

1950
The National Museum of Ethnology becomes a branch of The National Museum of Korea

1966
The Korean Folk Hall opens in *Gyeongbok* Palace, managed by the Office of Cultural Properties, predecessor of the Cultural Heritage Administration

1975
Museum hosts first special exhibition titled "Special Exhibition on Folk Photos"

1946
The National Museum of Ethnology opens on Mt. *Namsan*

1964
Museum receives first donation, a baby cradle

1975
The Korean Folk Museum opens in *Gyeongbok* Palace

before the government decided to demolish the building. The museum moved to its current site in 1993.

The current National Folk Museum building was originally designed to house The National Museum of Korea. The Office of Cultural Properties held a contest in 1966 for design of the new National Museum building and the National Treasure Construction Company's design was selected as the winning entry. The construction of the building began in November that year and was completed in 1972. The building was used as

The Korean Folk Museum, 1975 (*Gyeongbok* Palace formerly The National Modern Art Museum)

1987
Publishing of
academic study "Folk
Customers of Wido"

1989
Starts "Crafts Class
for Grandmothers
and
Granddaughters"

1993
The National Folk
Museum of Korea
reopens at its
present building in
Gyeongbok Palace

1993
Begins performance
Series "Traditional
Folk Culture
Hanmadang"

1979
Renamed The
National Folk
Museum of Korea

The National Museum of Korea was built based on a winning design. 1971(*Gyeongbok* Palace)

The National Museum until 1986, when it then moved to the Japanese Government-General Building. With its move into the former home of The National Museum in 1993, The National Folk Museum added The Children's Folk Museum in 2003. The National Museum relocated its current site in Yongsan, downtown Seoul, in 2005.

The National Folk Museum building is located in the northeast corner of *Gyeongbok* Palace, protected by the government as Historical Site No. 117. The museum can be accessed through the east gate of the palace, its visitors walking through the main palace buildings and gardens along the way to its cntrance.

The museum actually consists of three buildings built upon a massive stone foundation. The three buildings are connected through the museum's first-floor lobby and exhibition halls while the administrative office and archives have offices on the second and third floors.

Each part of the museum is modeled after traditional architectural masterpieces from among listed National Treasures. The columns and staircase of The museum's façade

1995
Publishes inaugural issue of "Folk Newsletter"

1994
Launching "Journal of Folklore Research"

1994
Starts cultural program "National Folk The Museum Visits Schools"

1995
Publishes study on village shrines in Seoul and Gyeonggi Province

1995
Hosts "Folk Culture Exhibition of Past 100 Years"

Reopening of The National Folk Museum of Korea

are inspired by the platforms and *Cheongungyo* and *Baekungyo* bridges of *Bulguksa* Temple in Gyeongju, North Gyeongsang Province.

The five-story main building is modeled after *Palsangjeon* Hall of *Beopjusa* Temple, while the three-story building on the east takes the form of *Mireukjeon* Hall of *Geumsansa* Temple. The two-story wing on the west is modeled after *Gakhwangjeon* Hall of *Hwaeomsa* Temple.

The form and structure of the museum reflects the intentions of the Office of Cultural Properties to achieve 'forms that are capable of duplicating existing historical objects,' as described in the bid manual in 1966. Back then, the idea of 'modern traditional architecture' was to basically take the key elements of traditional hanok houses, such as

Museum's central staircase, inspired by the *Cheongungyo* and *Baekungyo* bridges of the *Bulguksa* Temple in Gyeongju, North Gyeongsang Province.

the tiled roofs, columns, walls and platforms, and cut them out in concrete, and then paint them in traditional colors.

However, the obsession for imitating traditional architecture drew fierce criticism from architectural and cultural circles alike. It was difficult to ask for creativeness in the form and structure of the building when the main objective was to imitate an odd mixture of old architecture, and yet, somehow manage to fit in with the surroundings at *Gyeongbok* Palace. And there was little freedom to explore effective floor plans when the shape and structure of the building was predetermined. The National Folk Museum building, therefore, had clear limitations in space usage and functionality from the start, and the debate continues on the ways to construct contemporary buildings without

2000
Establishes Cultural Exchange and Education Division,
encourages Korean exhibition halls in foreign museums,
including National Museum of Popular Culture in Mexico City

2009
The Children's Folk
Museum reopened

1996
Hosts special
exhibition
commemorating 50th
anniversary of
museum

2002
Holds exhibition in Japan titled
"The Country Next Door: Japan"

2003
The Children's Folk
Museum Opens

2006
The Korean Life
Cycle Hall opens

Reopening of The National Folk Museum of Korea, 1993 (*Gyeongbok* Palace formerly The National Museum of Korea)

losing a sense of tradition.

Up the central stairway and past the stone flooring on the right is the museum's entrance. The current building was vacant for several years after The National Museum relocated to the Japanese Government-General Building. However, after a renovation effort by a local architecture firm, Space Group (*Gonggan Geonchuk*), and the redesigning of the exhibition rooms by interior design firm, *Hanjip* Design, the building reopened as The National Folk Museum in 1992. During the process, the court-type exhibition space, which was used by The National Museum to display Buddhist sculptures, was transformed into the National Folk Museum's special exhibition hall. The room is flanked by the museum's three permanent exhibition halls. However, the lack of connections between the museum's five-story main building, which was designed after *Bulguksa* Temple's *Palsangjeon* Hall, and the two other buildings limits the effectiveness of the upper floors as exhibition space. The inefficient layout has critics arguing that the museum's unique design and structure offers not much more than symbolic value.

The Opening of The National Children's Museum of Korea

Central hall's ceiling and walls, inspired by post-and-lintel structures of traditional houses

Considering the large size of many of the exhibited items such as model houses and historical relics, The National Folk Museum needs a space big enough to allow organizers freedom to explore new themes and ideas. However, the building's shallow, *Palsangjeon*-inspired upper floors and the web of pillars supporting the reinforced concrete structure have deprived the museum of an efficient floor plan. The building's layout was not the only problem. The lack of funding meant that the building didn't have enough storage room for ideal museum operations. And the restrictions in space often resulted in awkward floor plans that disrupted the flow between the displays and the direction visitors were expected to walk in. These were obvious problems, but not much improvement was made during the building's renovation process before The National Folk Museum moved into it in February of 1993. There were no meaningful changes in the building until the opening of The Children's Folk Museum in 2003. The museum also started a project to renovate its interior, a process that was completed in 2008.

The stone platform and granite surface are the distinctive features of The National Folk Museum building, and the same elements were also used in The Children's Folk Museum that opened in 2003. However, achieving cohesion between the museum's façade, distinguished by the stone platform and pointy structure of the main building, and its interior proved to be a difficult challenge. This was what the museum sought to solve as it started its interior improvement project in 2004.

As a result of the project, the museum created a wider lobby that was equipped with an information desk, coffee shop, a central hall and a lounge for visitors. The focus was to give the museum a contemporary touch, rather than remaining as an imitation of old styles, and the efforts to adopt modern elements in material, design, color and structure were evident. The post-and-lintel structure of the central hall's ceiling and walls, as well as their bright colors, the stone sinks of the restrooms, and the coffee shop connected to the grounds of *Gyeongbok* Palace are reflective of the efforts to modernize the museum's architectural elements. The changes directly affect the renovation projects of the museum's permanent exhibition halls between 2006 and 2008. Currently, the museum is

Stone sinks of restrooms

Gyeongbok **Palace and The National Folk Museum of Korea are centrally located in Seoul.**

attempting to improve its outdoor exhibition spaces in a effort that will continue through 2011. One of the ideas is to link the indoor and outdoor exhibition spaces by creating a mock-up of a traditional village and a contemporary city street in between.

A distinctive advantage of The National Folk Museum is that it is located on the grounds of *Gyeongbok* Palace. However, this also doubles as its biggest problem, as the expansion or remodeling of buildings within protected historical sites is strictly restricted by law. The lack of cohesiveness between exhibition planning and the building's structure has the museum facing difficulties in planning displays, providing educational programs and managing its collection.

A relocation of The National Folk Museum is inevitable, as *Gyeongbok* Palace is now undergoing renovation to restore its original appearance. In a new building, wherever that might be, the museum hopes to construct a space that better supports its goal of inspiring the present and providing vision for the future.

1 한민족 생활사

History of Korean People

❶ Inside the History of Korea: Timeline of Everyday Life

❷ People of this Land

❸ From Nature to Humanity: Paleolithic to Bronze Age

❹ Territorial Expansion: Three Kingdoms, Unified Silla and Balhae

❺ Flourishing Cultures: Goryeo and Joseon Kingdoms

❻ The Rise of the Urban Class: Opening Ports to 21th century

❼ Lives of Ordinary People: A Video

In the Hall of Everyday Life visitors will see a selection of objects and exhibitions related to the daily lives of the Korean people from prehistoric times to the present from both cultural and historical perspectives. The introduction features a timeline of Korean history as well as a wide selection of materials illuminating the lifestyles of the people who lived on the Korean peninsula.

Part I

'From Nature to Humanity' sheds light on the lives of prehistoric humans and the development of the skills which enabled them to use the natural surroundings to their advantage. The exhibit focuses also on how an increase in production from the Paleolithic to Bronze Ages led to the emergence of social classes and states.

Part II

'Territorial Expansion' examines the lives of people during the times of the Three Kingdoms, Unified Silla, and Balhae, as countries competed - by land and sea - to expand their territories and conquer neighbor states.

Part III

'Flourishing Cultural' reveals the development of typography and printing during the Goryeo and Joseon eras, as well as how the creation and promulgation of *Hangeul* (the native alphabet of the Korean language) contributed to the spread of knowledge and information to the general public. Also displayed are everyday items from these periods, which provide a glimpse into the lives of the people from these eras.

Part IV

'The Rise of the Urban class' focuses on the commonplace goods and living spaces of average Koreans from modern and contemporary periods. From the late 19th century, Korea was forced to open its ports and, with that exposure, began its transformation into a modern nation.

Part V

'Lives of Ordinary People' provides a visual presentation of the lives of ordinary people through the flow of time.

History of the Korean People

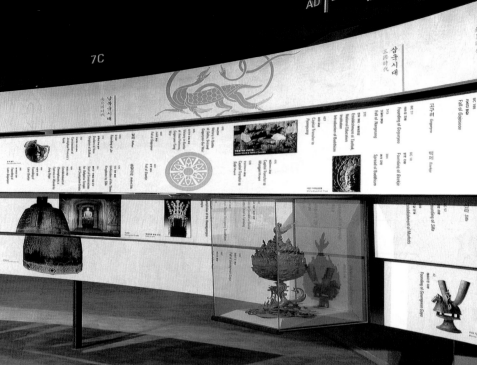

Timeline of Everyday Life

BC 2333
Founding of Gojoseon, First Korean Kingdom According to National Myth of Dangun Wanggeom

BC 700000
Beginning of Paleolithic Period

BC 194
Founding of Wiman Joseon

BC 57
Founding of Silla

BC 37
Founding of Goguryeo

313
Fall of Nangnang

394
Spread of Buddhism

475
Capital Transfer to Wungjin (Gongju)

BC 8000
Beginning of Neolithic Period

BC 1000
Beginning of Bronze Age

BC 4c
Beginning of Iron Age

BC 108
Fall of Gojoseon

BC 42
Founding of Geumgwan Gaya

BC 18
Founding of Baekje

372
Establishment of Taehak, National Education Institution / Introduction of Buddhism

427
Capital Transfer to Pyongyang

490
Establishment of Markets

신석기시대
新石器時代
청동기시대
靑銅器時代
신석기 문화 시작
Beginning of Neolithic Period
BC 2333
Founding of Gojoseon
by Dangun Wanggeom,
Gojoseon's Mythical
Founder (Samgukyusa)
청동기 문화 시작
Beginning of Bronze Age
철기 문화 시작
Beginning of Iron Age
빗살무늬 토기
Comb Pattern Po

502 Ban on Sacrificial Burial / Cattle Used in Farming

527 Royal Decree Accepting Buddhism

532 Fall of Geumgwan Gaya

538 Capital Transfer to Sabiseong (Buyeo)

562 Fall of Dae Gaya

566 Completion of the Hwangyong-sa Temple

612 Victory in Battle of *Salsu*, Second Goguryeo-Sui War

645 Victory in Battle of Ansi Fortress, Goguryeo-Tang War

660 Fall of Baekje

668 Fall of Goguryeo

676 Silla's Unification of Peninsula

698 Founding of Jin

713 New Kingdom of Balhae Founded

751 Start of Construction for *Bulguksa* Temple and *Seokgulam* Grotto

792 Construction of Princess Jeonghyo's Tomb

828 Establishment of *Cheonghaejin*, a Fortress in Wando by Jang Bogo

900 Founding of Later Baekje

901 Founding of Later Goguryeo

918 Founding of Goryeo

926 Fall of Balhae

935 Fall of Silla

936 Unification of Later Three Kingdoms

958 Introduction of Civil Service Examination

1087 Publishing of First Edition of Tripitaka Koreana

1170 *Musin Jeongbyeon*, Revolt of Military Officers

1251 Completion of Tripitaka Koreana

1363 Usage of Cotton

1377 Printing of *Buljo Jikji Simche Yojeol*, World' s Oldest Metal-Print Document

1392 Founding of Joseon

1402 Start of the Resident Registration System

1443 Creation of *Hunmin Jeongeum*, Early Version of Korean Alphabet (Promulgated in 1446)

1592 *Imjin Woeran*, Japanese Invasions of Korea

1708 Enforcement of *Daedongbeop*, UniformLand Tax Law

1876 Signing of Treaty of Ganghwa, Forced Opening of Korean Ports

1899
Opening
of Seoul-
Incheon
Line,
Korea's
First
Railroad

1919
March 1st
Independence
Struggle /
Founding of
Korean Provisional
Government in
Shanghai

1938
Ban of
Public
Use of
Korean
Language

1945
Liberation
from
Japanese
Occupation
(Aug. 15,
1945)

1950
Korean
War(1950-
1953)

1970
Start of
Saemaul
(New Village)
Movement/
Opening of
Seoul-Busan
Expressway

1987
Great
Struggle
of June
1987

2000
Summit
between
South and
North
Korea

2004
Opening
of High-
speed
Railroad

1894
Start of
Gabo
Peasantry
War

1897
Founding
of Korean
Empire

1910
Signing of
Japan-
Korea
Annexation
Treaty

1927
Start of
Radio
Broadcasting

1941
Declaration
of War
Against
Japan by
Korean
Provisional
Government

1948
Founding
of the
Republic
of Korea

1960
April 19
Student
Revolution

1980
May 18
Gwangju
Democratization
Movement

1988
1988 Seoul
Summer
Olympics

2002
2002 FIFA
World Cup
Korea/
Japan

The exhibited photos and relics show the many faces of Koreans who lived through the course of history, from prehistoric periods to the contemporary era.

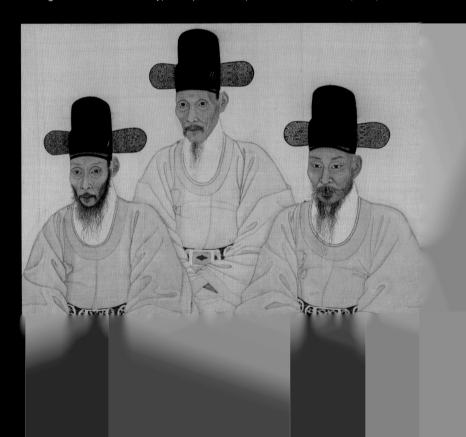

Dolls
1920

From Nature to Humanity: Paleolithic to Bronze Age

During the Paleolithic and Neolithic periods, people learned to cultivate and utilize nature rather than merely adapting to their surroundings. In the Paleolithic period, people frequently moved around to find better places for hunting and gathering food.

Later, they began to settle and started agriculture production during the Neolithic period. Stone instruments became diverse and sophisticated and earthenware was made for the

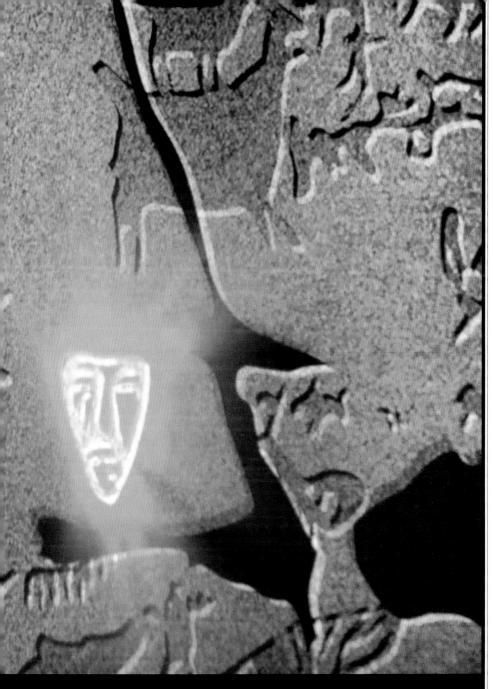

With the development of agriculture, people of the Bronze Age built houses similar to dugouts near rivers and coastal areas and established villages. Stone tools were primarily used, although bronze weapons were also produced as status symbols for political rulers. Increased agriculture production led to the creation of social classes and conflicts emerged among communities due to the need to acquire more agricultural products and cultivatable land.

Hunter-Gatherers to Pastoral Farming:
Paleolithic & Neolithic Ages

People in the Paleolithic period collected fruits, plant roots and hunted animals. For this purpose, they made coarse and crude tools from stones scattered in the fields or mountains. They had to move around constantly to locate better areas for food collection and hunting.

People began to live in their settlements as soon as they partly engaged in agriculture in company with fishing, hunting and gathering. They made sharp tools using stones and animal

bones. Ground stone tools were used for agriculture, hunting and fishing and as implements for everyday life. Typical farm implements at the time include sickles made of stones or animal bones, stone plowshares, stone hoes, grinding stones and plates for peeling husks and fruits. Arrows and bows for hunting, rods and nets used for fishing were among the advanced implements. As agricultural production developed, earthen vessels for transportation and

From Egalitarian to Stratified:
Bronze Age Village Society

An ethnic group of Tungus origin moved south from Manchuria and Mongolia and settled in the Korean peninsula in 10th century BC. They brought with them their bronze culture. Bronze Age peoples erected houses similar to dugouts on low hills or flat lands near rivers and seas, and established villages. The *Nonggyeongmun cheongdonggi,* a ritual artifact in bronze exemplifies the existence of dry-field farming with hoe and plow.

Carbonized rice has been excavated from sites in Heunamri, (Yeoju) and Songgukri, (Buyeo) while

remains of paddy fields in Majeonri (Nonsan), Okhyeon (Ulsan) point to the existence of rice farming. At this time implements such as bronze weapons, ground stone agricultural tools and various types of plain earthenware were made and used.

Advancement in agriculture resulted in an increase in production and in turn led to the emergence of social classes and the dolmen, stone cist graves, jar-coffin tombs and burial accessories which remain confirm this. This model Bronze Age village was based on the information gleaned from relics and excavated ruins.

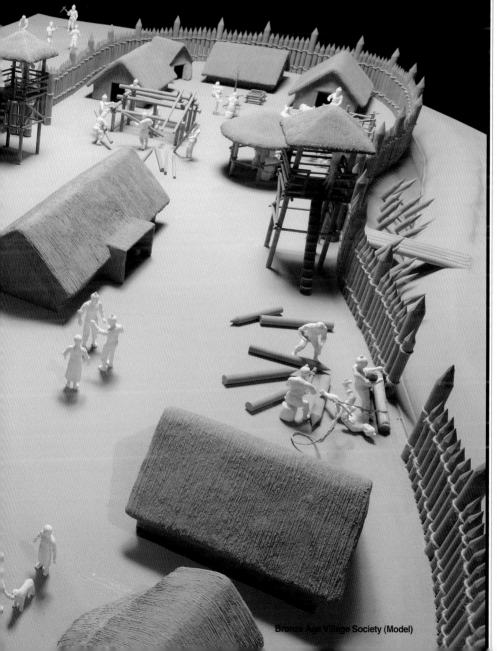

Bronze Age Village Society (Model)

Whales Swimming
in Groups

Prayer for Successful
Whale Hunt
Woman Spreading Her Arms
and Legs

Whale Hunting
Whaling Ship

Whaling Scene

Engravings of Affluence and Desire: Bangudae (Ulsan)

The Bangudae engraving, discovered in 1971, is found on the rocks of the Taehwa River in the southwestern city of Ulsan. This massive piece of rock art, measuring eight meters in width and two meters in height, is a state-protected cultural asset designated National Treasure No. 285.

Creating images on rock or other solid materials, and the development of sharp instruments used for this type of crafting, is indicative of late Neolithic and Bronze Age cultures.

Tiger, boar, rabbit, whale, turtle and fish were among the numerous animals engraved on the rocks, as well as a variety of geometrical patterns and images of the daily lives of people.

It is believed that the creators of Bangudae were expressing, through this art, a desire for bountiful returns in hunting

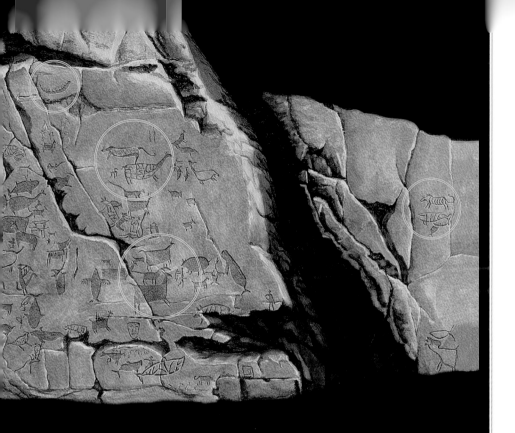

Land Animals

Boar, Deer, Tiger

Hunting Scene

Hunter With Bow

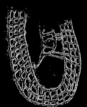

Hunting Scene

Net - fishing skills

Bangudae engraving

and fishing. This also points to the possibility that shamanistic rituals were common among people of this region. The images of animals confined by fences suggest that livestock farming was also being practiced.

The video, based on images from the rock, depicts the lives of late Neolithic and Bronze age people.

The First State: Gojoseon

The myth concerning the establishment of the first Korean state, Gojoseon, and its founder, Dangun, is described in *Samgukyusa* (Memorabilia of the Three Kingdoms), a history book written by Ilyeon, a Buddhist monk of the Goryeo period. Described in the *Samgukyusa,* rain, cloud and wind, were controlled by Hwanung, the son of Hwanin (Lord of Heaven), and thus were associated with agriculture while the three holy objects allude to the use of bronze tools and to the emergence of political rulers.

The relationship between Hwanung, the bear and the tiger reflected the relationship between different tribes and the process of conquest and integration that preceded the founding of the state. A wealth of Bronze Age relics have been discovered in the north-west of the Korean peninsula and on the coastline of southern Manchuria, once part of the ancient kingdom of Balhae.

In the 4th century BC, the ruler of Gojoseon crowned himself king. The influx of ironware culture over the following century allowed the political rulers of the kingdom to strengthen their power. The use of iron resulted in an increase in production and accelerated economic development. This also stimulated the forming of governing systems and *The Law of Eight Provisions* was imposed to obtain social order.

The Korean-type bronze dagger from this period is representative of the development of bronze and ironware culture.

Korean-type Bronze Dagger
Bronze Age
Property of Hengso Museum of Keimyung University

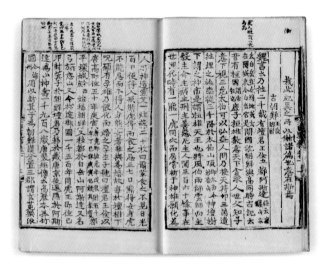

Memorabilia of the Three Kingdoms
Goryeo
Property of Kyujanggak, Seoul National University
Replica
A history book written by Buddhist monk, Il Yeon (1206-1289), in 1281, or the 7th year of the reign of King Chungryeol of the Goryeo Kingdom.
The book describes the history of Gojoseon, the first Korean kingdom.

Ironware and the Emergence of Ancient Kingdoms

When ironware was utilized for the first time in the 3rd and 4th centuries BC, mainly simple implements like axes and chisels were produced. It took another hundred years or so before ironware was more widely accessible and gained greater variety of use.

Iron - harder, durable and able to be made sharper than bronze - was useful in a wide range of tools including axes, hoes, plows, sickles and hand knives.

Broader use of iron enabled increased production, which in turn led to intensified conflict between different social groups over the distribution of goods. The outcomes of battles were largely decided by the superiority of iron weapons. This explains the rapid development of offensive weapons such as swords, spears and arrowheads as well as the defensive shields, helmets and armor.

The growth of production, the process of war and the integration amongst different social groups led to the emergence of the ancient kingdoms Goguryeo, Baekje, Silla and Gaya.

Iron Armor
Gaya
Property of Bokcheon Museum
Replica

Iron Sword with Ring Pommel
Gaya

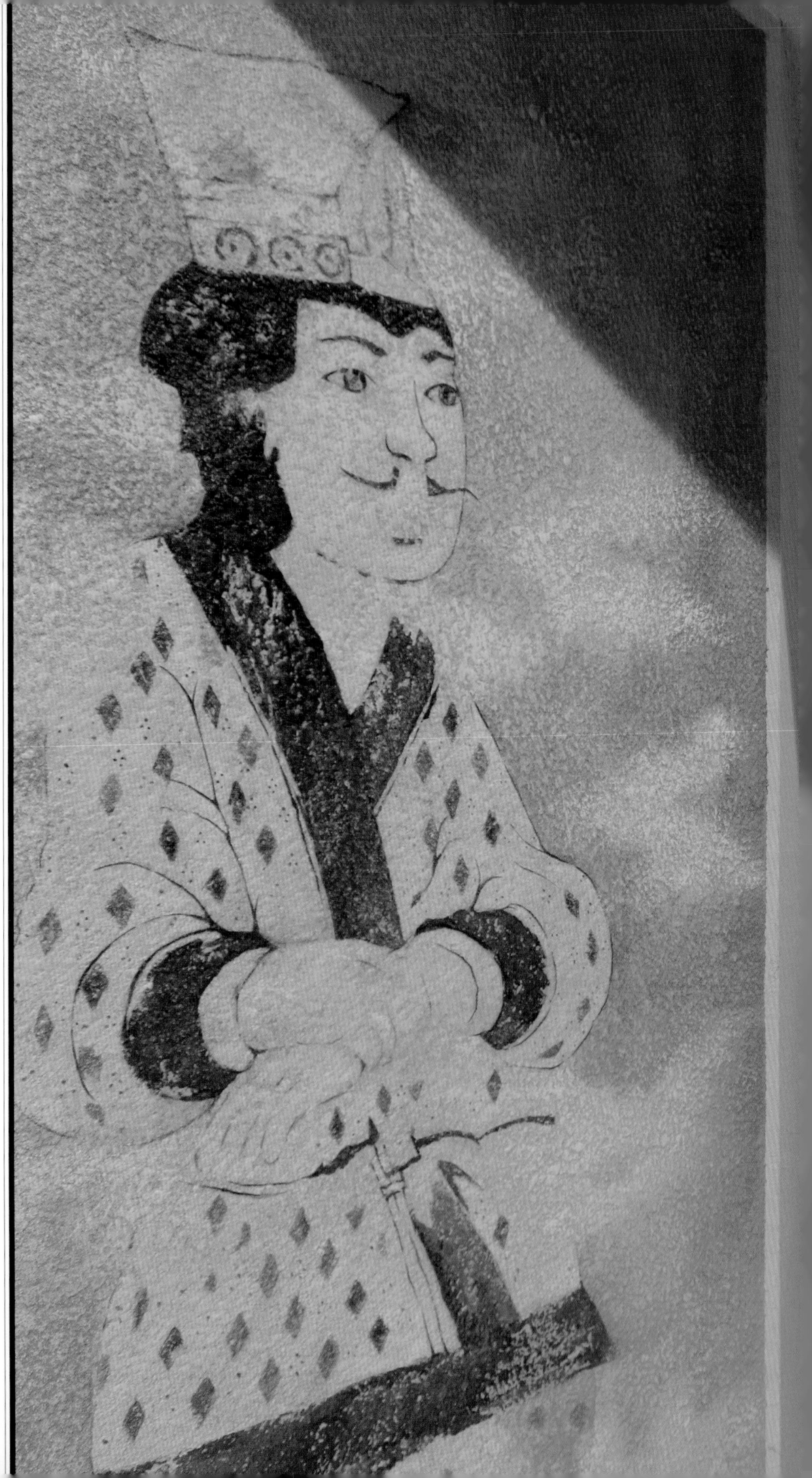

The Three Kingdoms period began with Goguryeo, Silla and Baekje conquering neighboring states. The growth of these states was heavily influenced by iron technology used in such implements as farming tools and weaponry.

The development of the Three Kingdoms inevitably led to the extension of the sphere of influence of the Korean people. The Three Kingdoms gradually formed a homogenous culture as they succeeded in both expanding their territories and maintaining consistent political systems to govern the inhabitants in the areas. The lives of people of that period were reflected in relics and vestiges including the mural paintings of Goguryeo.

The Three Kingdoms engaged in a continuous cycle of alliance and hostility, war and peace over several hundred years. A series of all-out wars eventually defined the fate of the countries in the 7th century.

Due to an incomplete unification of the peninsula by Silla, the founding of Balhae in the north (which inherited the tradition of Goguryeo) resulted in the formation of two Korean states: nominally north and south. After unification, for three hundred years, Silla attained a high standard of living, aligned with a vigorous Buddhist culture.

Balhae, associated with many northern ethnic groups and with its own developed culture, achieved a notable standard of living also and was named the 'flourishing country east of the sea'.

A Dream of a Vast Continent

Goguryeo, along with Silla and Baekje, was one of the Three Kingdoms that dictated the shaping of Korea's ancient culture. Goguryeo had a unique culture that also reflected influences from China and other countries.

Goguryeo was a major regional power of northeast Asia: sophisticated in politics and prospering in economy and culture. These are reflected in the ruins, relics, mural paintings and other cultural assets that remain.

The mural paintings of Goguryeo are usually devoted to describing moments in daily life. Also frequently discovered are astronomical charts and pictures of "The Four Guardian Gods." Images of social customs, cultural-religious events, art, clothing, craft and the technological skill of Gogureyo are all vividly represented.

This exhibition recreates the daily lives of Goguryeo people based on the images from the murals.

Life in Goguryeo through Mural Paintings (Video)

Balhae - A Flourishing Country East of the Sea

Balhae (698-926) was established by Daejoyeong, a former Goguryeo general. This kingdom was composed mainly of people displayed from Goguryeo, though the Malgal tribe also accounted for some of Balhae s population.

After a severe confrontation with China's Tang dynasty in the mid-8th century, Balhae was able to arrange diplomatic relations with Tang, Silla, and Japan. From the reign of its tenth king, Seon (818-830), to its thirteenth king, Balhae, then referred to as the flourishing country east of the sea, enjoyed the zenith of its prosperity.

Here the tomb of Princess Jeonghyo, the fourth daughter of King Mun, is recreated, in actual size, based on historical evidence. The tomb's chambers had painted brick walls, with three or four vaults built above them, topped by larger flagstones. A tower was erected above the tomb.

Using brick walls to divide the chambers shows influence from the Tang, while parallel vaults supporting the ceiling were synonymous with Goguryeo tombs. Erecting a tower above the tomb, however, represents a distinctive Balhae style

Skeletal remains of the princess, and her husband, were found in the tomb, as well as wall paintings, 12 people, a gravestone and ceramic human figures.

Tomb of Princess Jeonghyo (Reproduction)

The largest ritual site ever found in Korea is located in the village of Jukmakdong in Buan, South Jeona Province. Located on the highest point in the western part of the Byeonsan peninsula, the site provides a good view of the notoriously rough waters of Chilsan. It is believed that people performed rituals at the Jukmakdong site praying for safe travel on the sea routes.

Considering many of the ritual artifacts found here were identified as Baekje earthenware dating from the 4th to the 7th centuries, it is believed the site was created during the Baekje period. Since celadon and white porcelain artifacts were also discovered at the site, it is estimated that rituals were held here for close to 1000 years.

Celadon artifacts from China s East Chin (344-424) were also found at the Jukmakdong site, as well as a variety of weapons, horse tack and stone artifacts from the Gaya kingdom and Japan.

Baekje was known for its active exchanges with neighboring countries, including China, Japan and Gaya, therefore Jukmakdong clearly was a site where sailors of many kingdoms prayed for the safe passage of their trade-heavy ships before sailing to east or west.

8.

The *Samguksa* describes the ancient seaways as being open from the early time. Thus, the active exchanges from country to country are reflected in the variety of historical sites, relics and folklore that remain today. Jangbogo (?-846), a prominent maritime figure during the Unified Silla period, garnered a reputation for sophisticated shipbuilding and sailing skills. He opened the Cheonghaejin garrison on the island of Wando in South Jeolla Province, which contributed in broadening the transport routes connecting Japan and China. This also allowed Silla to take command of the neighboring seas.

Ritual artifacts, everyday goods and other relics discovered in the Cheonghaejin sites in Jangdo are representative of the time Jangbogo rose to prominence. The seaways pioneered by Jangbogo encouraged exchange between different peoples and cultures and also allowed Silla to benefit from vibrant trade.

Gold Crown From
Hwangnamdaechong
Tomb, Daereungwon
Burial Ground

Cheomseongdae

Millennium City: The Capital of Silla, Gyeongju

Gyeongju, variously called Seorabeol, Donggyeong or Gyeongdo, was the capital of Silla for one thousand years from the Three Kingdoms period to the Unified Silla period.

In every aspect - from the rise to the fall of the Silla kingdom - it was the political, economic, social and cultural center. Since the construction of Geumseong by its founder, Bakhyeokgeose, in 37 BC, Gyeongju became a planned city with the designation of urban districts in the twelfth year of the reign of King Jabimaripgan in 469. Following that time, and similar to modern systems, the administrative districts were divided into 160m × 140m square-shaped areas with each unit called a *bang*.

Later, Gyeongju grew into a great city with close to 900,000 residents, incorporating several surrounding districts and also drawing an influx of population from beyond those districts. According to *Samgukyusa*, Gyeongju - at the highpoint of its existence in the 9th century - had 178,936 houses, including 35 described as wealthy homes, in 1360 *bang* and 55 *ri*.

Here the 1/400 scale model of Gyeongju recreates the city's urban center at its prime. The video presentation features past and present images of the city s significant historical sites.

Roof-end Tile
Inscribed
'Jaeseong,'
Weolseong Palace
Site

Bronze Scissor
from Anapji

Nine-Story Wooden
Pagoda,
Hwangnyongsa
Temple

The Capital of Silla, Gyeongju (1/400 scale model)

The unification of the later Three Kingdoms and the founding of Joseon paved the way for historical development based on a truly unified nation. Confucianism functioned as the basic ideology underpinning politics and social order. Buddhism, which was popular among commoners, became the spiritual core of the state.

The centralization of power in the monarchy was achieved by the establishment and development of bureaucratic systems such as the *gwageo* (civil service examination) and regional governance. The development of typography and stable governance contributed to the spread of both knowledge and

1481
인종 상강행실 언니도 간행
Publishing of Vernacular Version of Samgang Haengsil Yeollyeodo

조식이 아비 죽으믈 보고
구챠히 살면

information. The creation and spread of *Hangeul*, the native alphabet of the Korean language, brought significant changes to the general populace, as they were able to express their ideas in a simpler written form.

The advancement of agricultural production and a monetary-based economy, accompanied by advances in agriculture, commerce, and crafts production during the late Joseon period, accelerated changes in social classes and growth in class-consciousness among commoners. As people were able to express their ideas and emotions, this provoked a wider range of participatory cultural activity.

Championing the Hopes of the People

Confucianism, which formed the political ideology of Joseon, was concerned with adapting principals of an ideal world to real society. This social philosophy is broadly represented in many Joseon astronomical and science studies artifacts and documents. The king, his power bestowed by the heaven, bore the responsibility to conduct state affairs on behalf of heaven. Naturally, one of the king's most important duties was to constantly observe those heavens – the sky and stars – so as to detect any changes in that 'will'.

The making of a new astronomical chart epitomized the kingdom's commitment to the will of heaven and to conduct state affairs accordingly in the interests of the populace. Thus, star chart production was a significant socio - political activity that garnered rapt attention.

Hemispheric Sundial
Joseon
A device that measures time by the
shadow cast from the sun.

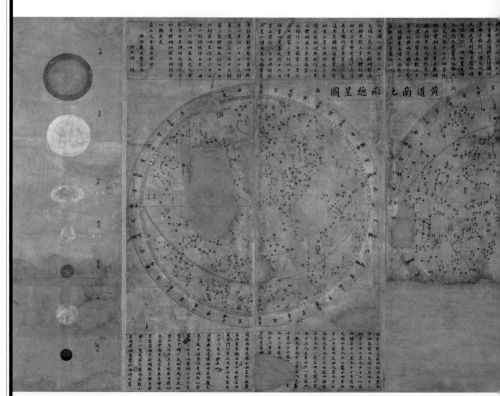

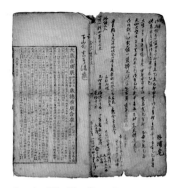

Annals of the Ming Dynasty

1580

Treasure No. 1319

An almanac is an annual publication containing tabular information, such as astronomical data and various statistics, arranged according to the calendar. The Daetongryeok was a Chinese almanac used by the Ming Dynasty and was imported in 1370 during the reign of King Gongmin in the late Goryeo Kingdom. The almanac, which was used until 1653 during the reign of King Hyojong of the Joseon Kingdom, was unique for its descriptions of activities that are to be encouraged or discouraged for each date on the calendar.

Angbuilgu - a sundial made for public display - was installed amongst the crowded streets with the time on the clock indicated by drawings, rather than written characters, allowing even the illiterate to read time.

Confucianism as a political ideology is clearly manifested in *Gyeongjikdo*, a drawing aimed at educating aristocrats in the process of agricultural production and of the effort that is required in the fields. Another tool representing the importance of agriculture, the *Cheukugi* - a rain gauge - was used for gathering seasonal precipitation data and thus the need to build water-control facilities.

New and Old Style Astronomical Chart

Early 18th century

Treasure No. 1318

Astronomical charts, used to identify and locate astronomical objects such as stars, constellations and galaxies, were not merely celestial coordinates used by astronomers, but also doubled as status symbols.

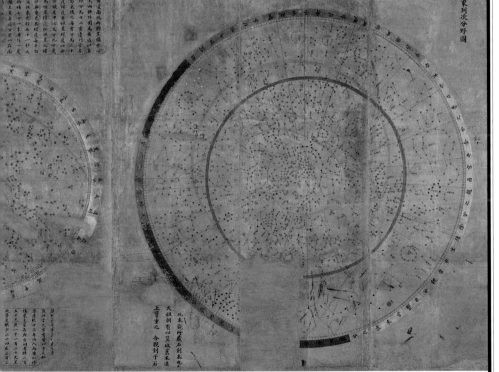

Hope Expressed in Written Characters

From the Unified Silla period the popularization of the Buddhist scriptures helped in the development of the Korean printing technology.

Mugujeonggwangdaedaranigyeong, discovered in the *Seokgatap* stone pagoda of the *Bulguksa* temple, is the oldest known wood block used for printing in the world, and is assumed to have been made before 751 when the *Seokgatap* was built. In the Goryeo kingdom, the publication of *Daejanggyeong* promoted large-scale wood-type printing. The production of the Tripitaka Koreana (*Palman Daejanggyeong*), which embodied the commitment to overcome Mongolian invaders with the spiritual power of Buddha, represents the most advanced typography technology of the time.

The advancement in metal-type printing within the Goryeo kingdom resulted in the publishing of the 50 books of *Sangjeonggogeumyemun,* in 1234, during the reign of King Gojong.

Baekunhwasangchorokbuljojikjisimcheyojeol, published during the reign of King U (1377), is the world's oldest existing metal-type document. In the early Joseon period, the creation of the metal type Gyemija (1403), Gyeongjaja (1420), and Gapinja (1434), marked the completion of the Joseon metal-type printing style. The development of metal-type printing and wood block printing, until late Joseon, significantly contributed to the acceptance of Confucian culture.

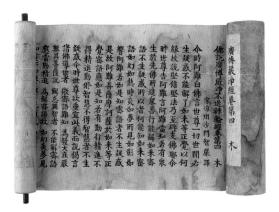

The first manufactured Tripitaka
11th century

Pure Light Dharani Sutra
Unified Silla
Replica

Woodblock Pure Light Dharani Sutra
Unified Silla
Replica

Proper Sounds for the Instruction of the People: *Hunminjeongeum*

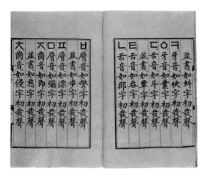

***Hunminjeongeum*, The Korean Script**
Joseon
Replica

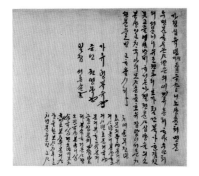

Home Sale Document Written in Korean
1811

King Sejong (1418-1450), the fourth king of Joseon, created *Hangeul*, the native alphabet of the Korean language, motivated by the needs to allow common people, illiterate in Chinese characters, to easily read and write.

The phonemic alphabet was completed in late 1443, Sejong's 25th year as king, and was promulgated through the edict, *Hunminjeongeum*, in 1446. *Hangeul*, composed of 14 consonants and 10 vowels, is one of the rare alphabets of the world in that there is a known inventor and clear period of creation.

Although the project to create *Hangeul* faced fierce opposition from the elite, Sejong never wavered from his commitment and pushed the process forward by ordering royal scholars to compose the *Yongbieocheonga*, a poem that represents the first piece of literature written using the new Korean alphabet. *Hangeul* allowed a far greater number of people to express their thoughts in writings. This brought significant changes to the life of the average person, who could now exchange letters with relatives and friends, participate more fully in community matters (such as civil petitions and public proposals) and share knowledge of agricultural skills. This increase in information, created and accessed by the public, contributed both to an improvement in living conditions and a development of social consciousness.

A Letter in Korean written by Empress Myeong Seong
Late 19th century

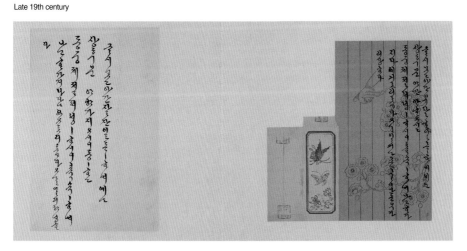

Art Found in Daily Life: The Rediscovery of Lifestyle

Dramatic socio-economic changes during the late Joseon period altered the course of Korean history. The growth of the peasantry, which coincided with the disintegration of the traditional social class system, resulted in a strengthening of class-consciousness among commoners. This also meant that cultural items, formerly solely enjoyed in their sheltered world by the social elite, were now available to a broader range of people.

White porcelain and *buncheong* ware, two of the distinctive styles of pottery during the Joseon era, are good examples of this. While aristocrats savored the elegant, jade-green glaze of Goryeo celadon, the simple beauty of Joseon's milky-white ceramics and bluish-green stoneware was identified equally with the social elite and commoners.

The culture of the general populace is well represented in pottery produced throughout the Goryeo and Joseon periods. The most distinctive examples are found in the late 17th century Joseon pottery styles of

cheonhwa porcelain, distinctive for its design patterns drawn using iron pigments, and _seokganju_, dark brown pottery used primarily for food storage.

Commoners who had gained wealth through commerce created a trend of decorating their houses with genre paintings or _minhwa_, literally 'popular paintings'. These were themed using mythical figures and other traditional objects. These paintings were often the work of anonymous craftsmen who adhered to inherited styles and genres from the past.

After the 18th century, increased production and demand for paper led to a growth in the publication of documents, books, paintings, calligraphic collections and other materials, and also inspired a trend of paper-made handicrafts and artwork.

Tobacco, imported from Japan between the late 16th and early 17th centuries, emerged as an important commercial product for farmers, and had a significant impact on the expansion of the economy.

Life Expressed in Ceramic Vessels

The diversity, beauty and evolving styles of pottery reflects changes in society over the course of time. The use of kilns, or thermally insulated chambers, inspired an evolution in pottery from earthenware to ceramic. In Goryeo, ceramics became popular for everyday use and this led to mass production. However, celadon porcelain, characterized by its elegant jade-green glaze and sophisticated patterns, was chiefly available to the royal and noble classes. The art of Goryeo celadon attained its peak during the 12th and 13th centuries with the emergence of *sanggam cheongja*, which possessed distinctive decorative elements including inlaid designs.

In Joseon, white-powdered celadon porcelain produced in various forms, after celadon porcelain, was widely used in the 15th and 16th centuries. White porcelain, which reflected simple and practical Confucian style, was brought to its apotheosis.

The bluish-green ceramic ware of *buncheong* also became popular during the 15th and 16th centuries of Joseon alongside the stylish white porcelain whose milky-white ceramic embodied the purity of the Confucian spirit.

White porcelain was developed into a variety of styles, adopting the colors of sea green, brown and red while *cheolhwa* porcelain, distinctive for its iron pigment decorations, was a unique Joseon product.

The increased production of white porcelain meant that not only nobles but also commoners were able to own these beautiful objects. It was during this time that unglazed pottery, used as dishes or jars for storing and fermenting foodstuff, began to emerge as a significant style in Korean pottery and develop diversity both in form and design.

Bottle, White Porcelain
Joseon

Jar, *Buncheong* Ware
19th century

Bottle, *Buncheong* Ware
Joseon

Jar, White Porcelain
Joseon

Bottle, Red Ocher
18th century

Jar, Red Ocher
18th century

Flat Bottle
20th century

Dubyeongdeuri, **Oil Bottle**
20th century

Sikchobyeong, **Vinegar Jar**
19th century
Donated by Kim Jeong-gi

Paper: The Tree's Gift

The increase in the production of paper after the 18th century meant that paper was used for much more than just in the publishing of books, written documents, drawing or painting.

The exhibition here features a variety of paper-made handicrafts, which represent a unique Korean art form that emerged during this time. Covering wooden boxes with decorative papers and brushing them with black lacquer or oil produced paper-covered boxes and flower-pattern boxes used to keep clothing, books and other items.

This display also includes artifacts made by weaving paper fibers, a technique used to produce not only small vessels but large basins also.

Paper Woven Flat Flask
Joseon

Paper Woven Vessel
19th century

Paper Woven Basket
19th century

Tobacco

Tobacco is believed to have reached Korea from Japan in the late 16th or early 17th century. The tobacco cases represent a broad range of styles, some with simple designs and others with lavish decoration. Clearly, tobacco was, initially, an indulgence for all classes.

However, commoners later faced restrictions in the consumption of tobacco, hence the popular saying that 'the length of the pipe represents the social status of its owner'. Tobacco emerged as a lucrative commercial crop in the late 18th century with an increasing number of farmers 'cashing in' and becoming wealthy from its local cultivation.

Tobacco Box
Early 20th century

Tobacco Pipe, Pipe Cleaner
Early 20th century

Tobacco Pipe Rack

Joseon

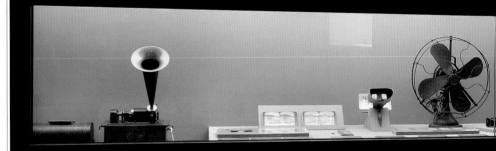

The Rise of the Urban Class:
Active Populace, New Culture

Korean society experienced unprecedented change in the century past. Japanese imperialism and colonial rule, liberation, division of North and South, modernization, industrialization and globalization initially brought despair and frustration to the public, but allied to that a sense of achievement with the overcoming of such difficulties in the 21st century.

In Korea the development of material culture, science and technology has engendered an

urbanized population that is the main source of the nation's production and consumption. In this process, widely accepted western values have transformed the traditional patterns of food, clothing, housing and the lifestyle of the general populace. Over the past century, despite growing pains in the aftermath of such rapid change, the emergence of a dominant urban class is complete.

Facing the World:
Opening Ports, Enlightenment

Following the Treaty of Ganghwa in 1876, which forced Korea to open up to Japanese trade, the increased influx of foreign intellectual, cultural and industrial materials affected every aspect of Korean everyday life, replacing and often conflicting with elements of traditional culture.

The introduction of what we would now see as simple and basic - fuel, electricity, phonographs, matches, cigarettes, dyes, candles, clocks, lamps, textile, needles and cosmetics - brought dramatic changes to all Korean people. Those people who could enjoy the new goods' functions and comforts perceived such products as symbols of the Korea's progress towards modernity.

Stereoscope
Early 20th century

The stereoscope, an optical instrument with two eyepieces used to impart a three-dimensional effect to an image, was one of the distinctive items representing the early 20th century.

First Encounter with Matches and Western Tobacco

An illustration published in the British magazine, *The Graphic*, describes Joseon people seeing matches and western tobacco products for the first time.
Dec. 12, 1888 *The Graphic*

A person listening to a gramophone
1915
The Christian Gateway into Asia,
Word Outlook

Camera

1907

Made by ROUGH TONS in England

King Gojong, the 26th king of the Joseon Kingdom and first emperor of the Korean Empire, had his photography taken on March 16, 1884, to express his determination for 'enlightenment'.

Oil Lamp

Late 19th century-Early 20th century

Oil lamps, one of the distinctive products that symbolized the influx of Western civilization, were widely used in the early 20th century.

Phonograph

Early 20th century

Horace Newton Allen (1858-1932), an American diplomat, brought Korea's first gramophone in 1866, the 3rd year of King Gojong of the Joseon Kingdom.

Electric fan

1910s

This is an electric fan produced by the United State's
General Electric Company, which was established in
1892. Electric fans were first used by Koreans during
the early 20th century.

Herman Sander's Journey

Herman Gustav Theoder Sander (1868-1945), then as an army lieutenant, was assigned to a post at the Embassy of Germany in Japan on Dec. 6, 1905. He arrived in Tokyo in February of the following year and worked there until April of 1907. He then returned to Germany through the Siberian Railway in May of 1907. During his stay in East Asia, Sander was dedicated to collecting materials about the current Russian-Japanese War. He was also a frequent traveler, touring Sakhalin in August of 1906, the Korean Peninsula in the following month, and then visiting Yeosun, Daeyreon, Mokdan and other Chinese cities in November.

Photo of Herman Sander Standing Next to a
***Jangseung* (Totem Pole)**
Sept. 18, 1906 PM2:50
Donated by Stefan Sander

During his travels, Sander developed a keen interest in Korea, which had in him visiting the peninsula again in March of 1907. He also wrote about the country's unique culture and beautiful landscape while touring Seoul, the Mt. *Bukhan* Fortress and Sunwon.

Sander left a large collection of materials related to Korea, which included pictures, photographs, post cards, letters, official documents and artifacts.

The photographs were mostly taken by Nakano, a Japanese photographer Sander hired as his assistant. The 335 photographs that remain today were found chronologically arranged in a photo album.

Although his time in Korea was too short for Sander to gain a profound understanding of the country's culture, the photo captions written by him nonetheless shows an impressive level of insight.

This partially owes to Sander's friendship with people like Choi Tae-kyung, a teacher from the Dukeu School founded by Johannes Bolljahn, Goh, a Korean interpreter, and Nam Kyung-se, a man he met in Sungjin, North Hamgyeong Province.

Postcard
Mar. 28, 1907
Donated by Stefan Sander
A postcard sent by German army lieutenant Herman Sander to his son, Hans, who lived in Königstein. On the back of the post card is a photo of the streets near the *Daedongmun* Gate in Pyongyang.

Travel-themed Photo Album
1929
Donated by Stefan Sander

Album of Folk Paintings

1907

Donated by Stefan Sander

These genre paintings were drawn by a Korean artist in 1907
upon request by Hermann Sander. The images provide
detailed descriptions of Korean people during the time.

The Rise of the Urban Class and Changes in Daily Life:
The Japanese Colonial Era (1910-1945)

The process of modernization continued at pace under the repressive period of Japanese colonial rule. The people's lives were swiftly and drastically reshaped in both direct and indirect ways.

Railways and trains altered the people's experience of space and time. Improved standards of hygiene lowered the risk of health problems and new foods and condiments, introduced from other cultures, were

Recorded music from phonographs was often heard in the streets, while the stores that lined them were displaying and selling Western suits, dresses, hats and cosmetics.

Makeup:
A Further Dimension to Beauty

Foreign cosmetic products, which flooded Korea after the opening of the ports, were, at first, mostly applied by upper-class women but began to be used by a broader range of women during the 1920s.

Inspired by Western and Japanese products, a local company began producing the first domestically made cosmetic - *Bakgabun* - around this time. A wider range of cosmetic goods, including pomade, lotions, creams, perfumes and soap continued to be imported as they gained popularity for neat packaging and ease of use.

Mass newspapers and magazines frequently printed articles on the choosing and storage of cosmetic products, as well as directions for home-made alternatives. All the writings about 'white skin' and 'makeup tips' provide a guide to the beauty trends of the time.

Lady of Jesus Church
Early 20th century
From the Collection of Herman Sander

Cosmetics
Early 20th century
This is the first Western-type modern cosmetic product produced by a Korean company. The products were first used as free gifts given to cloth buyers at fabric shops, but its manufacturer later made and sold them as stand-alone items due to their popularity.

Train and Passengers

Sept. 27, 1906

From the Photography Collection of Herman Sander

Introduction of New Systems: Modern Medicine and Sanitation

The introduction of Western medical systems brought changes to medical practices and also to the traditional concept of disease and hygiene.

A variety of drugs, such as *Geumgyerap*, *Indan*, *Geonnoehwan*, *Hwalmyeongsu*, *Jogoyak*, *Yeongsinhwan*, *Palbodan* and *Cheongsimbomyeongdan*, were produced - and consumed.

This was also a time when pesticides - used for exterminating flies, mosquitoes, lice, fleas and bedbugs - made their first appearance, which also contributed to an improvement in hygiene standards.

Cardiac Stimulants
Early 20th century
A cardiac stimulant made by an early
Korean pharmaceutical company.

Pain Killer
Early 20th century
An anodyne produced by Korean
pharmaceutical company, *Yeonggi
Daeyakbang*.

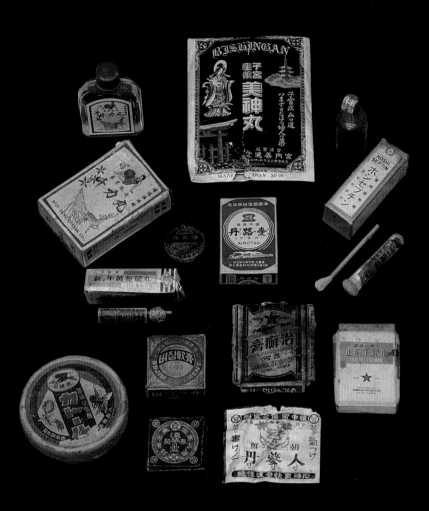

Modern Medicines

Early 20th century

'Miracle on the Han River' Urbanization: Progress Since Liberation

The late 20th century was a dynamic yet challenging time for Koreans, as they succeeded in pushing forward the nation's rebuilding process. In 1945, when the country was liberated from Japanese colonial rule, Korea's *per capita* income was around US$4. Now, the country's *per capita* is greater than US$20,000. Koreans tout this dramatic economic progress as the 'Miracle on the Han River.'

Through the course of economic development, Koreans began complementing traditional culture with modern and practical values. The advancement in digital technology has opened new directions in the lives of people, while the growth of popular culture has resulted in greater diversity.

Houses: The Past 100 Years

The style of Korean houses changed dramatically over the last 100 years. The traditional house, with its wooden floors and tiled roofs, gave way to Western-style houses, apartments and villas. The introduction of Western and modern Japanese houses in the late 19th century inspired a new trend in homes that mixed in traditional characteristics and the new influences. These included the urban *hanok* (traditional Korean

Apartments emerged as contemporary symbols of modernization and modernity since the 1945 Liberation and they remain the dominant, and most conventional, form of housing today.

Desk & Bookstand
1970s

Telephone
1970s
An early model of the automatic telephone.

Wall Clock

1960s

Television

1970s

An early television model produced by

Samsung.

Changes in Residential Space: The Kitchen

The kitchen, long considered a space reserved for Korean women, has undergone considerable change over the passage of time. In traditional Korean houses, kitchens were a separate space removed from the main building and used for both cooking and heating. They little resemble the contemporary kitchen, which has moved inside the house and is often equipped with cutting-edge appliances and equipment.

The structure and role of the traditional kitchen's fire hole changed in the 20th century when briquettes began to be used as the main fuel for heating. Inside the cupboards, vessels made of nickel silver and

Another wave of change was brought by the use of gas. Cooking and heating were separated in Western-style kitchens - installed in apartments since the 1960s - and kitchens now took their place adjacent to the living rooms. An increase in the variety of electronic appliances also resulted in confirming the unique-function profile of the modern kitchen.

Lives of Ordinary People: A Video

Here are images of Korean people of today - and of the past. The faces shown are not those of national heroes or celebrities, but of those who refer to themselves simply as ordinary people. History often focuses on major events or great people, but the experiences of the everyday men, women and children, those who lived through such changing times, are often missed - even neglected. Yet, in the images of these ordinary Korean people - from both yesterday and today - we maybe can catch a glimpse of our tomorrow.

2
한국인의 일상
韓國人 日常 The Korean Way of Life

❶ Establishing a Village / Organizing the Villagers
❷ Spring
❸ Summer
❹ To Market
❺ Autumn
❻ Winter
❼ Epilogue

The Korean Way of Life exhibition sheds light on the everyday lives of ordinary people during the Joseon period (1392-1910); lives which revolved around agricultural activity and were thus greatly influenced by the cycles of nature.

The items displayed provide a glimpse of life in a traditional Korean village with its food, crafts and folk art. The exhibit is designed to conjure up the feeling of walking through a centuries-old village. Also recreated is a traditional Korean market place, which doubled as a center for the commercial and leisure activities of the community.

The Korean Way of Life

Establishing a Village

According to the theories of *feng shui*, the best place to establish a residential area is between a river and a mountain. This ideal position - *baesanimsu* - translates as 'river in front, mountain in back'.

Many Korean villages are located according to the *baesanimsu* theory. Practically, the advantage of having a mountain sealing the village at the rear was that the range blocked the bitter northwest winds of winter making it easier for villagers to collect firewood and herbs. The river flowing in front of the village was used for drinking, cleaning and farming.

Jangseung, or village guardian, is a totem pole that was traditionally placed at the edge of the village to mark its boundaries.

Koreans also believed that the *jangseung* dispelled demons and protected villagers from illnesses. The poles were usually made of wood and had painted or carved human heads. Male *jangseung* figures were named *cheonha daejanggun*, which translates as 'guardian of the universe'. Female figures were named *jiha yeojanggun* or 'woman guardian of the underground'.

Sotdae, a tall wooden pole or stone pillar with a wooden bird on top, was often erected next to a *jangseung*.

Jangseung Hill

Hongsanhyeon jido, Map of Hongsan-hyeon

19th century

A map of Hongsanhyeon, near current day Buyeo in South Chungcheong Province. The village described in the map is a typical example of a traditional Korean rural neighborhood, with a mountain shielding the village from the back and a river flowing in front of it.

Organizing the Villagers

A village is where people of different social status, jobs and age coexist, and, in most traditional Korean communities, residents discussed and established their own rules for self-governance. The rules defined the relationship between the village and its neighboring communities; the standards for reward and punishment; and also mandated participation in communal activities.

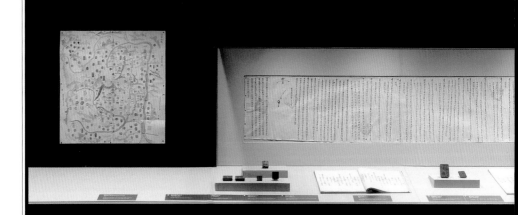

Paldeungmyeon Hyangyak Seonsaengan (Naming Local Level Officials)

1893

A document listing the names of local level officials who were selected to enforce *hyangyak*, or traditional village contracts that operated as an informal common law.

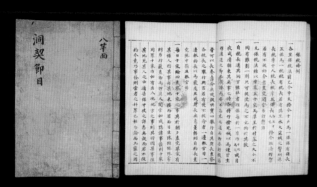

Donggeyjeolmok, Record of Local Community Regulations

19th century

The book records the laws and regulations governing a *donggye*, a local community unit of the *Paldeung* township of Sunchang, North Jeolla Province. The content of the book offers some examples of the self-imposed rules and rewards by local communities to achieve order and stability.

Korea's Seasonal Divisions and Customs

Traditionally, Korea has been an agriculture-oriented society. Political rulers throughout history have published varieties of almanacs, which included calendars with weather forecasts, astronomical information and the like for use by farmers.

Koreans traditionally used the lunar calendar, and also used a lunisolar calendar that divided the year into 24 solar 'terms'. Each division lasted around 15 days and was synchronized with seasonal changes. Many Korean customs and cultural events remain in accord with those solar terms today.

Cheonseryeok, Almanac

Late Joseon

During the Joseon Kingdom, a new king would mark his coronation by promulgating a new calendar. This symbolized the establishing of the new order, as well as informing farmers of the new agricultural season. On one side of the calendar was the Chinese sexagenary cycle of the year, the date and time of the 24 lunisolar seasonal divisions, and various astronomical data and statistics.

Siheonseo, Almanac

1887-1904

An almanac that arranged tabular information based on both the theories of the lunar calendar and solar calendar. Based on the annual cycles of nature, the almanac divided a year in 24 seasonal divisions and 72 subdivisions.

Myeongsiryeok, Almanac

1908

An almanac published in 1898 after the establishing of the Korean Empire. The content of the almanac is basically identical to the *Siheonseo*, with the tabular information arranged according to the lunar calendar and the dates and weekdays of the solar calendar written under each date.

Yonggapgyeong, Almanac

19th century

An almanac that marked the changes in the *yin-yang* cycles across the 24 seasonal divisions of the year. The first part of the almanac describes the nine phase in the changes of *yang*, while the later-half describes the nine phases of the changes in *yin*.

Figures of 12 Zodiac Animals (Repica)

Spring

According to the traditional calendar, spring is between the solar term of *ipchun* (February 4) and *gokwoo* (April 20), and was regarded by farmers as the sowing period. Every spring, the government encouraged farmers to achieve a productive agricultural season, and villagers performed ritual prayers for a good harvest and good fortune for the village throughout the year. Typically, the farming season started with the planting of rice.

In seaside villages, where fishing was the main activity, sacrificial rites were held for an abundant catch and calm waters throughout the year. To survive the *bori gogae* (spring famine) before the barley harvest, villagers sought wild herbs in the mountains and hills - though often they had to settle for weed-roots and tree bark instead.

봄

24절기의 입춘(立春 : 2월 4일 경)부터 곡우(穀雨 : 4월 20일 경)에 해당하는 기간으로 농작물을 파종하는 시기이다.
봄이 되면 나라에서는 농사에 힘쓸 것을 권하고, 마을에서는 일 년 농사의 풍년과 평안을 기원하며 마을의 수호신에게 제사를 지냈다. 농촌에서는 논밭을 갈고 거름을 주며 파종을 함으로써 농사를 시작 하였고, 어촌에서는 어로의 안전과 풍어를 위해 뱃고사를 지내고 '또다'라 할 수 있는 샛별에게도 어획을 풍성히 이루어진다. 산과 들에서는 나물을 캐고 보릿고개를 넘기 위해 풀뿌리나 나무껍질 등을 채취하기도 한다.

Spring

In spring (from February to April based on 24 seasonal divisions), the government encouraged the activities of the farming year and most villages performed a ritual ceremony to assure an abundant harvest and good fortune throughout the year. As rice-planting started, the farming year began. In fishing villages a sacrificial rite was held for the sea-god to assure a safe passage on the seas and an abundant catch. Also, spring is the time when shellfish are harvested in the foreshore. During the farm hardship period, farming people had a difficult time to find food. In especially bad circumstances, people had to survive by eating grass roots and the bark of trees on the mountains.

Royal Message for Agricultural Improvement

During the days of the Joseon Kingdom, the king hosted an annual ritual at the palace on Lunar New Year's Day in hopes to ensure abundant agricultural production for the upcoming farming season. King Jeongjo was particular for issuing orders to regional governors on every Lunar New Year's Day to encourage local farmers to improve agricultural production.

Commoners also performed a variety of ceremonial events on Lunar New Year's Day in praying for a good harvest. Rites dedicated to the guardian gods of the village were held at village shrines or other locations. In the sea villages along the eastern coast, locals held rituals for Haerangshin, or goddess of the sea, to ensure safe sailing and good catches. The ceremonial acts included sculpting the shape of a male penis in wood as a gift to the sea goddess.

Nonggajipseong, Guide for Farmers

17th century

An agriculture book written by Sin Sok (1600-1661) under orders of the king. Another well-known Joseon Kingdom agricultural book is the *Gwonnonggyomun,* published under the orders of King Sejong, which is famous for a passage that described agriculture as the fundamental source of all clothing and eating.

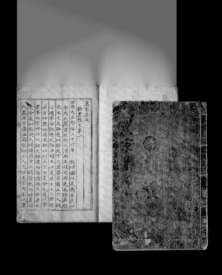

Plowing

Plowing was one of the first agricultural activities for farmers each year. They fed the ground with fertilizers and broke up the frost-hardened soil with plows. The use of oxen, which enabled farmers to plow deeper, was critical in increasing agricultural production.

❶ *Janggun*, Manure Cask Used for Collecting Urine
20th century

❷ *Janggun*, Manure Cask Used for Collecting Urine
20th century

❸ *Gwittaedongi*, Spouted Jar
20th century

❹ *Ttongjige* (Manure Carrier Yoke) and Ttongtong (Manure Bucket)
20th century

❺ *Janggun*, Manure Cask Used for Collecting Urine
20th century

Fertilizing the Land Folk Painting on Farming Early 20th century

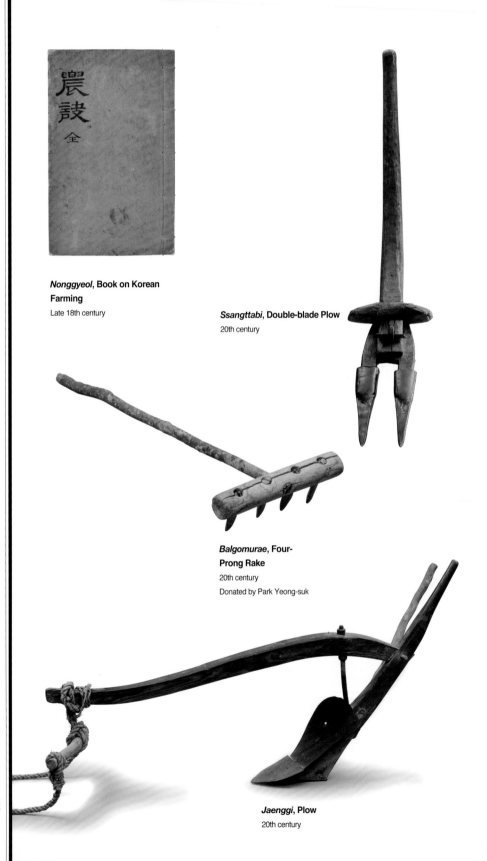

Nonggyeol, Book on Korean Farming

Late 18th century

Ssangttabi, Double-blade Plow

20th century

Balgomurae, Four-Prong Rake

20th century

Donated by Park Yeong-suk

Jaenggi, Plow

20th century

Plowing the Field Folk Painting on Farming Early 20th century

Working in Rice Paddy Folk Painting on Farming Early 20th century

Namtae, Field Roller

20th century

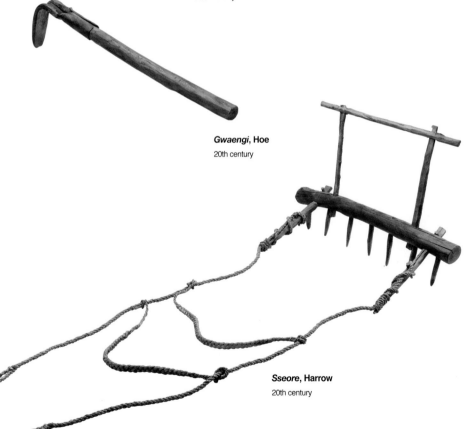

Gwaengi, Hoe

20th century

Sseore, Harrow

20th century

Farmer Flags and Peasant Music

Dure was a uniquely Korean type of collective labor activity that was frequently conducted by small farming communities. Farmers in the village worked together on each other's farms during the busiest times of the farming season and this collective work was critical in achieving desired levels of agricultural production.

When farmers headed to the fields for the day's work, they often walked together under a *nong-gi* or farmer flag. During breaks, they often played drums, gongs and other musical instruments to relieve their

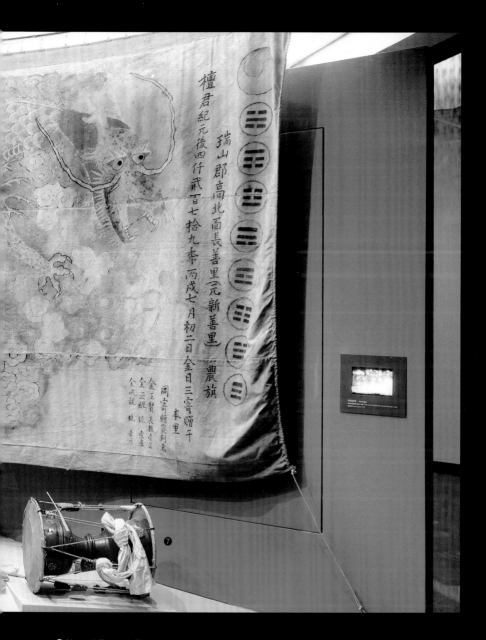

檀君紀元後四仟貳百七拾九年丙戌七月初二日全日三壽贈于

瑞山郡高北面長善里(元新善里)農旗

金匠賢長載壹員

金云經錯壹座

金成龍鐥壹坐

同寄顯員列名

本里

① *Nonggi*, Farmer's Flag

1946

A flag carried by farmers during dure, a type of collective laboring operation within small farming communities. This flag, which was used in a village in Seosan, South Chungcheong Province, is distinctive for is drawing of a dragon, which symbolizes cloud and rain, and a carp, standing for an abundant farming season.

② *Sangmo*, Spining-tasseled Hat

20th century

③ *Jing*, Gong

20th century

④ *Buk*, Drum

20th century

⑤ *Sogo*, Hand-Drum

20th century

⑥ *Kkwaenggari*, Hand-held Gong

20th century

⑦ *Janggu*, Hourglass-shaped Drum

20th century

Foreshore Farming

Tidal flats are coastal wetlands formed when mud is deposited by tides: exposed at low tide, underwater at high. The areas are known for their abundance in marine life, including oysters, octopus, clams and crabs.

There is an old Korean saying that 'farming in tidal flats is ten times more productive than land farming'. Spring was the time when oysters, clams and ark shells broke from their winter hibernation and moved back toward the surface of the mud. Fishermen on Korea's southwest coast were particularly busy harvesting at this time.

***Josae*, Oyster Hammer**
20th century

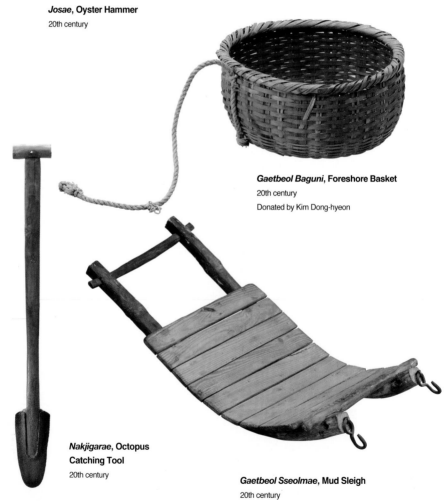

***Gaetbeol Baguni*, Foreshore Basket**
20th century
Donated by Kim Dong-hyeon

***Nakjigarae*, Octopus Catching Tool**
20th century

***Gaetbeol Sseolmae*, Mud Sleigh**
20th century

Oyster Catching
Photo by Seo Heun-kang

Shellfish Catching
Photo by Seo Heun-kang

Gathering Wild Herbs & Famine Relief

Spring was when wild herbs like mugwort, *nengi* (similar to shepherd's purse) and rocambole were found in mountains and fields around the village. Aside from their good taste, these herbs were critical as food stuff for farming families in overcoming the '*bori gogae*' or 'spring famine.'

However, the gathering of these wild herbs also signified poverty. It was difficult to find food during the 'spring famine', when the grain stored away against the winter had been consumed and the planted crops had yet to ripen.

In the worst case, people had to survive on weed roots and tree bark. The government carried out a variety of famine relief policies to help farmers during the difficult spring period.

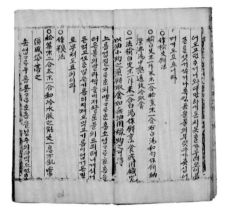

Guhwangbang, Tips for Beating Famine
Late Joseon

Vegetable Bag and Weeding Hoe
20th century

Picking Herbs Folk Painting on Farming Early 20th century

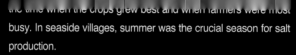

the time when the crops grew best and when farmers were most busy. In seaside villages, summer was the crucial season for salt production.

Saecham, the light meals between field work, and *nodongyo*, the traditional work songs of farmers, are a unique part of the culture of Korean farming communities. Leisure activities such as *daedong nori*, where villagers were grouped in teams for a 'catch-the-tail' game, were also important events.

Farmers took their summer naps in *ramie* or hemp clothing worn to stay cool under the sun.

여름

24절기의 입하로부터 : 5월 5일 경부터 대서 大暑 : 7월 23일 경에 해당하는 기간으로 뜨거운 햇볕에 의해 농작물이 성장하는 시기이다.

모내기와 김매기·풋대치기 등에는 고된 노동이 수반되는 만큼, 이때 나타나는 새참과 노동요 풍속 등은 노동의 힘겨움을 함께 하는 즐거움으로 승화시키는 삶의 지혜였다. 김매기가 끝나고 나면 호미씻이와 더불어 한 판 대동놀이도 벌였다. 바닷가 염전에서는 강한 햇볕에 의해 소금이 만들어졌다. 한낮 더위에 지친 사람들은 한잠을 자거나 낮잠을 통해 휴식을 취하고, 무더운 여름을 건강하게 나기 위하여 모시와 삼베로 시원한 여름옷을 만들어 입었다.

Summer

Summer (from May to July based on 24 seasonal divisions) is the best season for growing crops and making a good quality salt with plenty of sunshine. As it was the busiest farming season, with an occasional day of relaxation equally as important as working hard in the fields. Farmers had saecham, - even today farmers do this - a light meal between regular meals in the field, and they enjoyed singing songs while working. Also after the busiest season of farming, they hold the entertainment events for the whole community. Koreans in the past developed a way of staying cool in the summer heat by taking a nap, and wearing clothing made of ramie or hemp.

Weeding & Light Meals

Pulling weeds, or *gimmaegi* is one of the most grueling activities during the farming season. An important tool - the weeding hoe - is distinctive for its large, arced blade. After the third round of weed pulling, farmers take a day off to relax and enjoy food and drink, a custom that is called 'hoe-washing'.

Saecham, or light meals between field work, is a tradition that continues into the farming communities of today. Of course, no in-the-field meal would be complete without *makgeolli*, the traditional, milky, rice wine.

Weeding Folk Painting on Farming Early 20th century

Bowls used for serving light
meals in a woven basket

Homi, Weeding Hoe
20th century

Kkakji, Bamboo
Thimble for Farmers
20th century

Tosi, Bamboo Wristlets
20th century

❶ *Salpo*, Spade for Irrigation Work
19th century

❷ *Dorongi*, Rain Coat
20th century

Water Management

Korean farmers would say that a successful farming season is dependent on the process of weeding (*gimmaegi*) and water management. The Korean weather is characterized by heavy rain during the summer, and relatively dry spring, fall and winter seasons. This meant that farmers needed smart strategies for water balance and management for their paddies and fields. Keeping rice seedbeds from drying was critical during the spring, while managing irrigation systems to prevent damages from floods or typhoons was a concern for the summer.

Before the use of machinery, it was common to see farmers scooping water into their paddies in buckets, or on rainy days, digging trenches dressed in raincoats to keep water from rising too high in the paddies.

Yongdure, Water Dipper
20th century

River and Sea

Summer was a time to enjoy catching fish and shellfish. The Koreans even named these activities - *cheollyeop* - fishing in the river and enjoying food and drink on the embankment.

Summer was also the best time to boost production in salt pans, due to the abundance of drying sunshine and wind. Salt produced during this time was used later in the year to make fermented foods and condiments such as *kimchi*.

Gari, Fish Trap
20th century

Tongbal, Fish Trap
20th century

Taewak and *Mangsari*(Buoy-net)
20th century

Muneodanji, Octopus Trap
20th century

***Mujawi*, Water Wheel**
20th century
Used for Providing Sea Water to Salt Farms.

Weaving

Traditionally, Korean women made cloth at home by weaving hemp, ramie, silk and cotton. The earliest mention of cloth-weaving traces back to the days of the Proto-Three Kingdoms Period. Aside from being used for making clothing, cloth was a critical revenue source for farming families and was also used as medium for exchange before the introduction of money. Home weaving was common until the later days of the Joseon Kingdom, when it began to fade due to the influx of modern fabric from the West and changes in consumption patterns for clothes. However, the traditional styles and skills of weaving continue in areas such as Andong, Hansan, Geumseong and Naju, with some of the artisans supported by the state as intangible cultural assets. The weaving of hemp was a long and laborious process that often had women in a village working together to reduce the amount of work for each other. This form of collective labor was called '*dure sam*,' and women participating in the operation often sang songs or competed in teams to make weaving more enjoyable. The variety of folklore, superstitions, taboos and folk songs related to weaving show how critical weaving was to traditional farming families.

Mulle, **Spinning Wheel**
20th century

Ssia, **Cotton Gin**
20th century

Beteul, **Loom**
20th century
Donated by Woo Bok-in

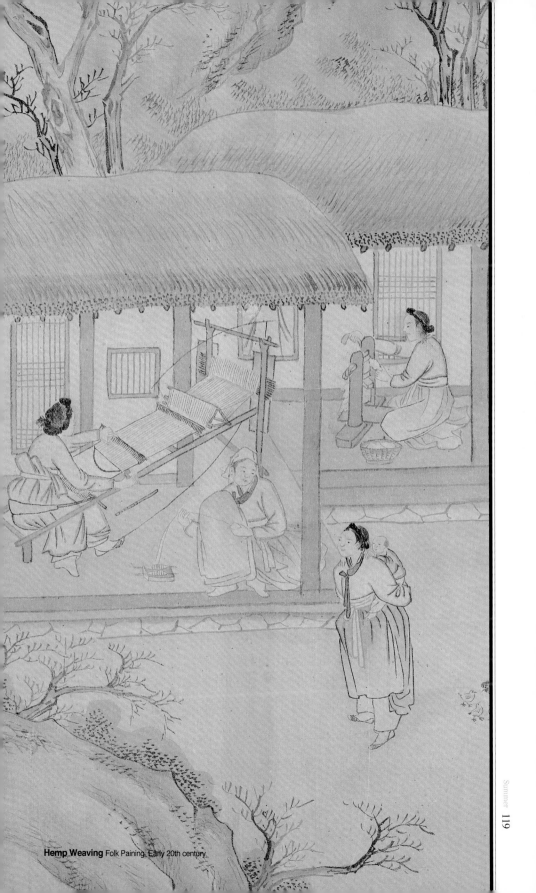

Hemp Weaving Folk Painting, Early 20th century.

Ramie and hemp fabrics were popular materials for summer clothing, because of their moisture absorption and open weave. Threads, made from ramie and hemp, were woven on traditional looms to produce the cloth.

Often, the fabrics were dyed in colors from natural pigments extracted from plants. *Deunggeori*, a rattan vest which was worn under jackets, and *tosi*, or wristlets, were also popular clothing items during the summer months.

The drumming of traditional ironing sticks to pound the fabric smooth was a unique and familiar summer sound.

Summer Rest Folk Painting Early 20th century

Napping

After finishing the process of weed pulling (*gimmaegi*), the intensity of farming work eases until the autumn harvest. In summer, farmers often take naps in the shade to escape the heat and recover from the hard labor. In the house, bamboo blinds, which block sunlight and yet provide ventilation, and companion bamboo benches - a frequent destination for naps - were some of the ways to fight the sorching summer heat.

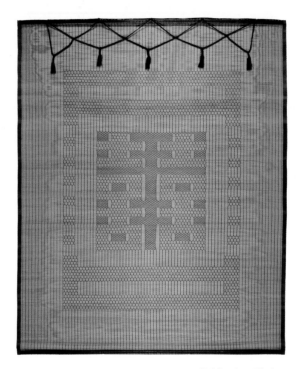

Bal, Bamboo Blind
19th century

❶ Jukbuin, Body-length Bamboo Pillow
20th century

❷ Hapjukseon, Folding Fan
19th century

❸ Paldeokseon, Fan
20th century

❹ Jukchim, Bamboo Pillow
19th century

❺ Pyeongsang, Bamboo Bench
20th century

The market was of pivotal importance to the farming community. Here merchants and craftsmen sold a variety of goods at their stores, farmers from different regions mingled to trade or sell livestock and street performers added to the already lively atmosphere.

The invention of calculating tools, the expanded use of money, and improvement in road conditions contributed to the vibrancy of markets and the rise in their numbers and frequency. Historical records state that during the early Joseon era, when everyday markets were first established, there were more than 1000 markets operating nationwide.

Grocery Store

Sangjeon were earlier versions of Korean grocery stores that sold a variety of items from books to horsehair, leather, candles beeswax and threads. The stores could be found in a number of markets in Hanyang, the old name of Seoul, including in front of *Euigeumbu*, southern part of *Jongnu*, or near *Angukbang*. *Sangjeon* basically sold just about everything. Photos from the late Joseon era show that the stores handled items such as combs, mirrors, scissors, glasses, pouches, knives and robe belts. Canes were a popular item as well, as the old saying goes "likely to soon use a cane bought from a *sangjeon*," which means that the person in question isn't likely to live much longer due to health problems or other reasons. There is also an old saying that goes "like a *sangjeon* merchant tightening his strings," used to describe a person's tight grip on a certain object. The phrase reflects the typical appearance of merchants who distributed and sold products at *sangjeon*, as they usually carried their items in sacks strapped to their backs.

Glasses and *Angyeongjip*
(Eyeglass Case)
19th century

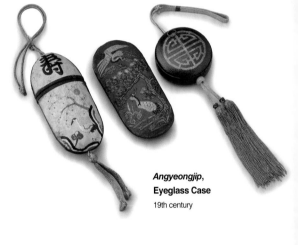

***Angyeongjip*,**
Eyeglass Case
19th century

❶ *Eollebit*, Comb
20th century

❷ *Songeoul*, Hand Mirror
19th century

❸ *Chambit*, Fine-toothed
Bamboo Comb
20th century

❶

❷

❸

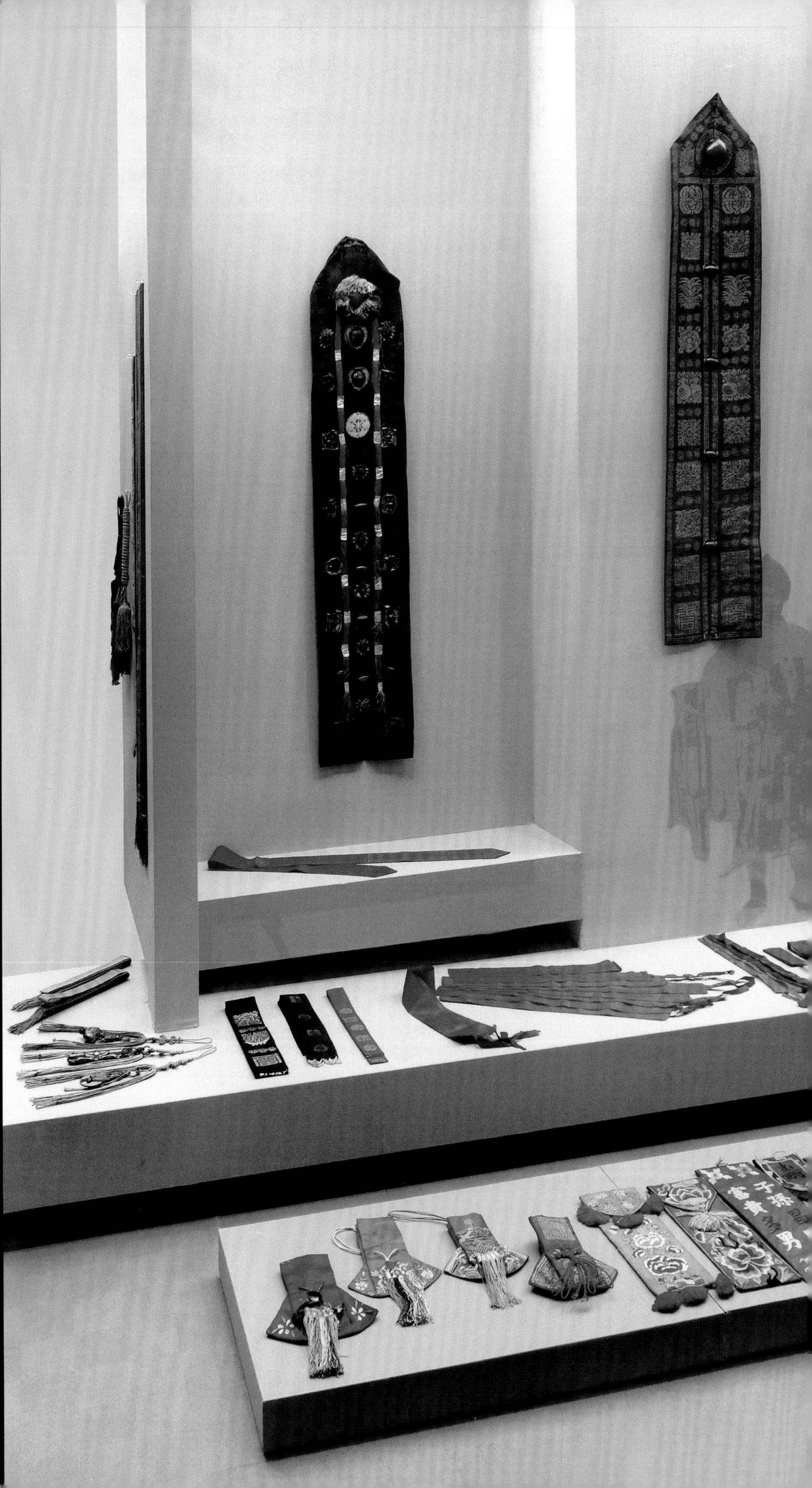

Sellers of a variety of ribbons and strings

Rental Shop

Semuljeon were shops where people rented ceramic dishes or brassware used for ceremonies, such as weddings or funerals, and also other items such as tables and straw mats. And it seems that *semuljeon* also rented clothes. In the famous *Bongsan Talchum* mask dance, there is a passage where the main character, *Malttuki*, guides a group of poor scholars to the civil service exam in Hanyang and blames their poor appearance on their rented clothing from a *semuljeon*

Hat Shop

Mojajeon, or hat shops, were called by different names depending on the types of hats sold. The stores selling the traditional black horsehair hats were called *heukripjeon*, while those selling the white hemp hats worn on state funerals were called *baekripjeon*. The stores selling *manggeon*, or traditional black head wrappings worn under hats, were called *manggeonjeon*, while shops selling hats made from fur were called *jeonripjeon*. The stores selling straw hats, or *chorip*, worn by young men after their coming-of-age ceremonies were called *choripjeon*.

Brim Repair Shop

Yangtaejeon were stores that made or repaired the brims of the cylindrical black hats, or *gat*, worn by high-rank government officials. The brims of gat were called *yangtae*. The width of the brim in gats differed depending on the bureaucratic status of the owner. *Gat* were fragile, could be easily damaged and required careful handling.

Shoe Store

Shoe stores, or *sinbaljeon*, had many different names depending on the types of shoes sold. The stores that sold cow-skin shoes, straw shoes, hobnail shoes and leather shoes for women were called *iseojeon*. Stores selling straw shoes and hemp shoes were called *seunghyejeon*. Wooden shoes worn on rainy days were sold at *chonuljeon*, which also handled a variety of items made

Jipsin, Straw Shoes
20th century

Mituri, Hemp Shoes
20th century
Donated by Ye Byung-min

Jipsinteul, **Frame for Making Straw Shoes** 20th century

Fabric Store

Fabric stores, or *pomokjeon*, were called by different names based on the type of cloth sold. Cotton was sold in *myeonpojeon*, silk in *myeonjujeon*, ramie in *jeopojeon* and hemp in *pojeon*. Cotton and silk were particularly valuable as they were used as mediums for exchange before the use of money. From the days of King Seonjo to the mid-19th century, *myeonpojeon*, *myeonjujeon* and *jeopojeon* were included in *yukuijeon*, or government-approved stores that owned exclusive rights for selling six types of goods

Gawi, Scissors
20th century

Pobaekcheok, Ruler for Measuring Cloth
19th century

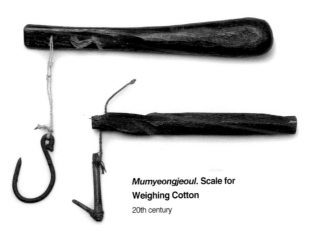

Mumyeongjeoul. Scale for Weighing Cotton
20th century

Peddler Merchants and Inns

The *bubosang* or peddler merchants were those who made the Korean marketplace unique. *bubosang* actually refers to two different types of merchants - the *busang* who carries his items wrapped in cloth, and *bosang* who prefers to carry his goods on his back.

bubosang moved freely and frequently between markets across the country, carrying maps and identification certificates that were provided to merchants with state licenses. *Gaekju* was another type of merchant who provided food and accommodation to the *bubosang*.

Bubosang Sinpyo, Identification Card for Peddler Merchant
1898

Bubosang Immyeongjang, License Certificate for Peddler Merchant
1902

Jeongnipyo, Record of Distance Between Regions
Joseon

Tujeonpae, Korean Playing Cards
18-19th century

Golpae, Domino-like Blocks
19th century

Weights, Measures and Calculating Tools

Rules, scales and calculating tools were a vital part of market life. The *Jucheok* - a traditional ruler about 23 centimeters long - was used for measuring lengths. The scales during this time weighed objects by the measurement standards established during the reign of King Sejong, with the each weight unit named: *pun, don, nyang, geun* and *jing*. The *hop, doe, mal* and *seok* were tools for measuring volume.

A widely used calculating tool of that time was the *sangaji*, while the abacus only appeared in markets during the 18th century.

Sanmok, Counting Sticks
20th century

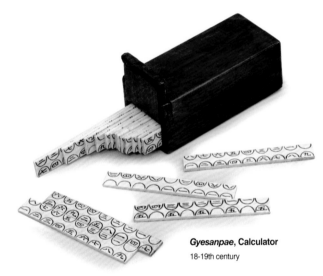

Gyesanpae, Calculator
18-19th century

Jupan, Abacus
19th century
Donated by Choi Yeong-chang

Jeoul, Scale
19-20th century

❶ Hop ❷ Sodoe ❸ Doe ❹ Mal
20th century
Units for measuring weight and volume. One *hop* is
equivalent to 0.18 liters, while 1 *doe* was 10 *hops*, or
1.8 liters. *Mal* was 10 *doe*, or 18 liters.

Money

Before the use of money, rice and hemp cloth were used as mediums for exchange. However, rapid economic development during the late Joseon period resulted in an increasing demand for currency. It was during the rule of King Injo that the *Sangpyeongtongbo*, the country's first coinage, was minted and circulated. In the 18th century, money became required in tax payment. With this law, cash was finally established as the main exchange medium and this contributed in the expansion of commerce.

**Yeopjeon and Yeopjeon
Gwae, Safe**
19th century

Entertainment

Sandaenori is a Korean traditional masked dance drama that was performed in the Songpa market in southern Seoul. This masked dance had to be performed in a large market because it required a significant amount of financial support.

Sandaenori combined dance, drama, pantomime and comedy, and was known for its sarcastic commentary on social issues such as the immorality of Buddhist monks and the corruption of the noble class.

Five Masked Thespians and Audience
From the Photography Collection of Herman Sander
Early 20th century

Yangjusandae Gamyeon,
Masks for Yangjusandae Play
Early 20th Century

Making *Soju*

Soju - a distilled beverage - is traditionally made from rice.
The *Sojutgori* is a distillation jar used by women for making *soju* at home.

The process of making *soju* is

1. Brewed rice wine is poured into a large iron pot placed over a fire, with the *sojutgori* fixed above the pot. The space between the *sojutgori* and pot is sealed with kneaded dough to prevent heat loss.
2. After a jar of cold water is placed above the *sojutgori*, the pot is heated, which causes alcohol in the rice wine to evaporate.
3. When steam reaches the jar of cold water at the top, the subsequent fall in temperature produces drops of *soju* that flow through a tube into the *sojutgori*.

Nuruk Teul, Mold for Pressing Yeast
Early 20th century

Dubyeongdeuri, Wine Bottle
20th century

Yongsu, Wine Strainer
Early 20th century
A strainer made from closely woven bamboo strips to collect clear liquor.

***Sojutgori*, Distillation Jar**
Early 20th century
Jar used at houses to make soju,
Korea's native distilled beverage

Chaesangjang

Chaesang refers to bamboo boxes made of woven bamboo strips. The bamboo strips are dyed in a variety of colors that gives the boxes a distinctive beauty. Traditionally, the boxes were used to keep clothes, needles and threads, and other household items.

Chaesangjang, or master craftsmen who still make these bamboo boxes, are designated by the Korean government as intangible cultural assets.

The making of a *chaesang* begins by selecting the right type of bamboo and cutting them into strips with identical thickness and length. The bamboo strips are colored with natural dye and woven to form boxes, before the craftsmen adds the finishing touches to give each box its own distinctive character.

***Chaesang*, Bamboo Box**
20th century
Boxes made of woven bamboo strips
used to keep clothes, needles,
threads and other household items.

Koreans traditionally needed a variety of mats for different purposes. Flimsy-woven mats were used in markets and other outdoor environments, while in the home the elaborately decorated *hwamunseok* were for visiting guests.

A variety of mats also meant a variety in materials, which included bulrushes, cattails and straw.

Hand looms were needed to produce the mats. The most common device was built on a frame of two T-shaped vertical shafts that had a long, wooden bar running across them.

A certain number of grooves were cut into the bar to place *godeuraetdol* or warp weights, which were used to tighten the warps. The fabric was then woven by throwing the weights back and forth with the transverse threads.

The 24 divisions on the traditional lunisolar calendar defines autumn as the period between August and October, a span that includes the harvesting season.

People during this time held ancestral ceremonies to express their gratitude for the yielded grain and fruit. Then the farmers thresh and polish rice. Some of the rice is saved as food reserve, while the remaining amounts were used to compensate hired hands or sold in markets.

The harvest marks the end of the farming season. Farmers then repair their traditional, straw-roofed houses in preparation for the winter.

가을

24절기의 입각으로는 : 8월 에서 입부터 시 살약이로 : 8월에 초반 온내 국식 하는 기간으로 농작물을 수확하는 자순걸이다 하는 시기아다. 중순에 대한 감사의 퍼례로 수추한 곡식을 조상에게 먼저 바치, 그 때에서 타작과 도정 과정을 거쳐 수확을 중 얼마는, 소무기 고, 또나도 얼바는 임배로써 거하마 등새 정화안무을 구임에, 쪼에게 나 가업에 거둡먼이한 국식과 복소압 검부이하여 판 새 농사는 맛수라, 주식가 오기 전에 창호지는 대로 바르고, 겨가겨월의 시혐을 준비는 둘 참수라와 하외 기준나라텀 데어진다.

Autumn

Autumn (from August to October based on 24 seasonal divisions) is the harvesting season. An ancestral ceremony is held, giving thanks for a good harvest with freshly harvested grains and fruits. After the process of threshing and pounding rice, part of the harvested grain was used for food and the rest went either for paying rent or for selling at the market. After the harvest, the farming year comes to end. With the end of the farm season, Koreans in the past repared their houses before the cold season came.

Expressing Gratitude

The major holiday of *Chuseok*, which falls on August 15 of the lunar calendar, is the Korean equivalent of the American celebration of Thanksgiving.

Some scholars believe that *Chuseok* may have originated from the ancient shamanistic celebrations of the harvest moon, and it is during this time that the country observes the largest full moon of the year.

During the holidays, an altar for ancestral rituals is set-up in each home adorned with that year's newly harvested grains and fruit as well as with 'holiday food' such as rice cakes and pressed candy.

***Tteoksal*, Rice Cake Pattern**

19th century

Harvesting

During the autumn harvest, farmers reaped crops such as rice, barley wheat, beans, corn and cotton. The harvesting of rice was considered the most important of crops.

After harvest, the grains and pulses were threshed and polished. Some were kept for food, while others were set aside to be sold at market.

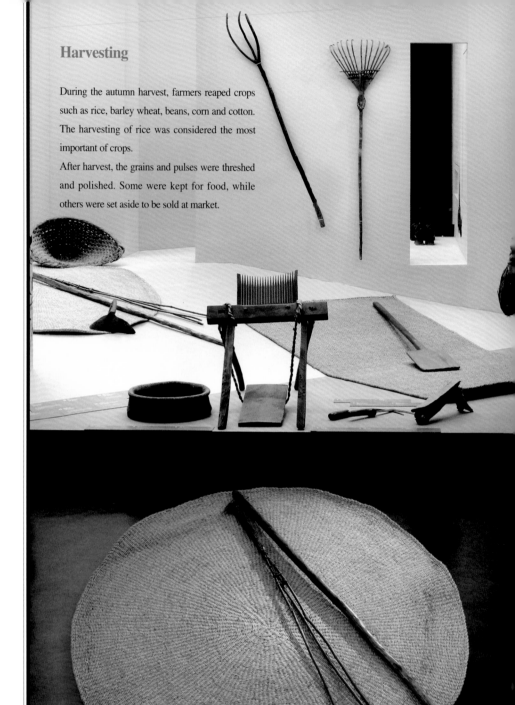

Dorikkae, Flailing Tool
Dorae Bangseok, Mat for Drying Grains
20th century

Harvest Folk Painting on Farming Early 20th century

Maetong, Wooden Mill for
Rice Hulling
19th century

Harvest Folk Painting on Farming Early 20th century

Sarangchae, Men's Quarter

In the traditional Korean house, *sarangchae* referred to the men's quarter of the house, which consisted of the *sarangdaecheong* (wooden floor), *sarangbang* (the man's study) and *numaru* (raised terrace).

Wealthy households often had a separate building used as the *sarangchae*. But in average

farmhouses, the *sarangbang* was usually the room that was located nearest to the gate. *Sarangbang* doubled as a personal and social space, used as room for receiving guests and educating children. This exhibited hanok (traditional house) is authentic, originally located at the Yongju village in Gyeongju, North Gyeongsang Province.

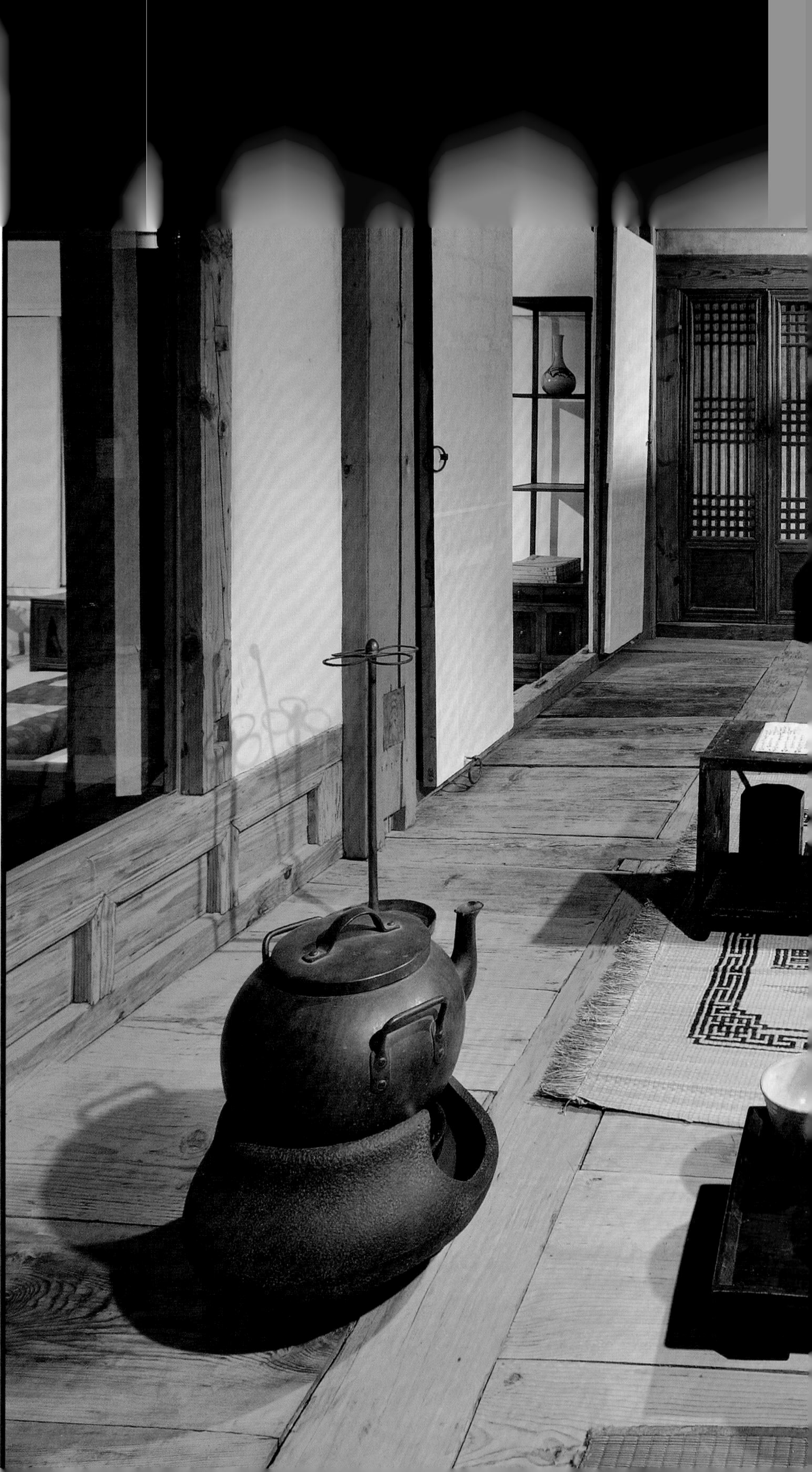

Numaru, Terrace

The *sarangbang* was usually connected to a raised terrace called a *numaru* that had elevated wooden floors and railings. In the *numaru* men read books or met guests over a cup of tea. This was also where tenant farmers met the house owner to pay rent and where the *mareum* calculated the collected rent and wrote documents.

Paying Farm Rent

Tenant farmers were those who farmed land owned by another person and who paid rent either in money or in-kind after harvest. Landowners hired *mareum*, or agents, to collect the rent and supervise the tenant farmers.

Gyeyakseo, Contract for Tenant Farmer
1915

Chusugi, Records of Farm Rent and Agricultural Production
1925

Sojak Daejangpan, Woodblock Template for Printing Farm Rent Document
20th century

Sajagyonghagi, Record of Expenditure from Farm Rent Income
1930
Donated by Hwang Yong-ju, Hwang Min-hwan

Paying Farm Rent Folk Painting on Farming Early 20th century·

In the traditional Korean house, *sarangbang* referred to the men's quarter of the house, which was separated from anbang, the women's quarter. Confucian ethics required that the living spaces of men and women be strictly separated.

The *sarangbang* doubled as personal and social space, used variously as a room for studying or receiving guests. It was equipped with a variety of writing materials and stationery items, and also a desk, box for documents and a case for rolled paper. Arm rests, cushions, pillows and folding screens were also among the common items found in the *sarangbang*.

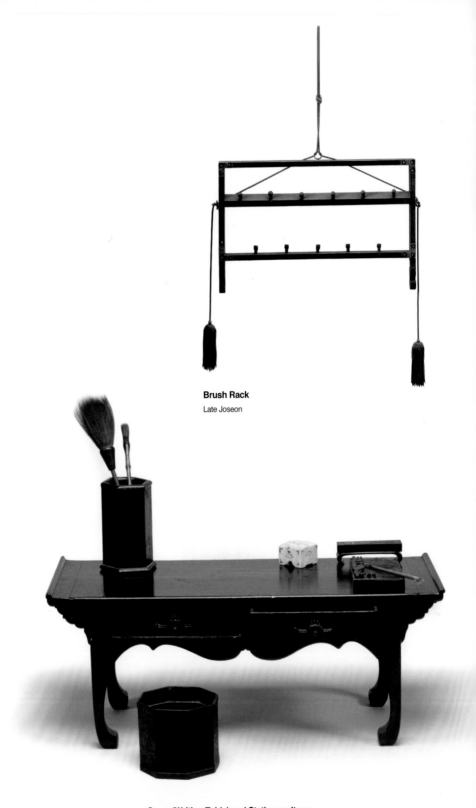

Brush Rack
Late Joseon

Seoan(Writing Table) and Stationery Items
Late Joseon

Four-Shelf Stand

Late Joseon

Repairing the House

At the end of the farming season, farmers finally found time to repair their houses to prepare for the approaching icy weather. Doors were covered with paper to block cold winds, while the holes on the walls were sealed to keep rats from stealing food.

Straw-roofed houses had their roofs repaired with new straw from the recent harvest. Houses with tiled roofs had any damaged tiles replaced. Farmers, who always had to be able to turn their hands to these repairs, kept a variety of wooden tools for just these occasions.

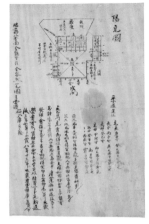

Yangtaekdo, House Location Record
20th century

Tanggae Top, Saw
20th century

Singan Jeungyangiseon Sangtaegyeonggyeong, Theories on Selecting House Sites
Early 15th century

Kkakkwi, Adze
20th century

Daepae, Plane
20th century

Geumeugae, Line Marker
20th century
Donated by Choi Bu-bong

Meoktong, Ink Line
19th century

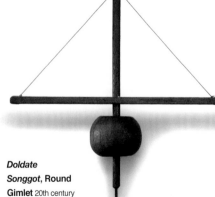

Doldate Songgot, Round Gimlet 20th century

Roof Making | Folk Painting, 20th century

Winter, according to the 24 seasonal divisions, is from *ipdong* - around November 8 - to *daehan* - about January 20.

After securing their food stores, farmers saved seed from their crops after harvest for re-planting in the next growing season. Hunting became important during the winter, when food became short. Tofu, made from beans, and kimchi (fermented cabbage) were also made traditionally during the cold weather. Padded clothing, hats and wristlets were all part of winter attire.

On the shortest day of the year - *dongji* - people ate red bean porridge, which was believed to dispel demons and ensure good fortune in the coming year.

Hunting

Snowy days were considered an ideal time for hunting animals. Traps were set on the hills and mountains near the village, in the hope of snaring pheasant.

Oebal Changnal, **Spearhead**
19-20th century
Donated by Kang Hui-seon

***Seolpi*, Snowshoes**
20th century

***Dunggunisin*, Snow Boots**
20th century

***Sseolmae*, Ski**
20th century
Donated by Lee Gang-bok

Chang, Spear
19-20th century

Kkwong Changae, Pheasant Trap
20th century

Jurumak, Knapsack
20th century

Hwayaktong, Gunpowder Flask
19th century

Jochong, Firelock Gun
18th century

Hunting Folk Painting 20th century

Salted Game Meat

Pheasant, boar and other game were important food sources in the winter as people couldn't afford to consume too much grain.

People held ancestral rituals on the day of *nappyeong* to offer the animals they had hunted and to share the meat with others after the ceremony.

Seoksoe, Gril
19th century

Jilhwaro, Earthenware Charcoal Burner
20th century

Jeongol Naembi (Casserole),
Hwaro (Burner)
19th century

Jeongol Naembi (Casserole)
19th century

Eating Salted Game Meat Genre Painting Replica

Anchae, Women's Quarter

Anchae, or the inner quarter of the house, was the living space for women and was consisted of *daecheong* (wooden floor), *anbang* (mistress' room) and *jubang* (kitchen). In the traditional house, the living spaces of men and women were required to be strictly divided. A small wall, called naewoedam, separated the anchae from sarangchae, or the men's quarter. In this exhibit, a glass wall is installed between the anbang and *sarangbang* (man's room) to symbolize the naewoedam.

Anbang was where the mistress of the house carried out her daily life, such as giving birth and raising children and doing housework such as making clothes and sewing. The room was furnished with wardrobes or keeping clothes and bedding and also a variety of items related to dressing and makeup. Paintings of flowers and birds often decorated the rooms as symbols for peace and fertility.

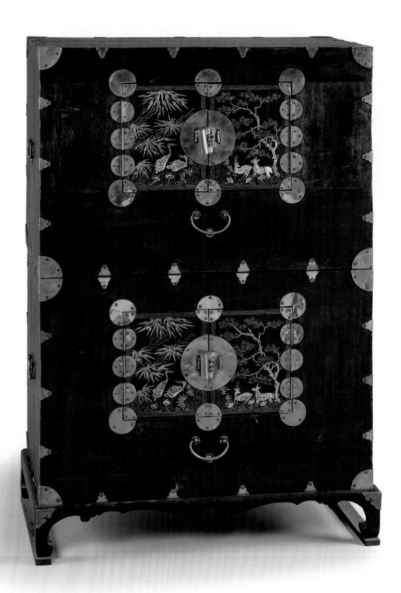

Najeon Icheungnong,
Clothing Chest Designed
With Mother of Pearl

Late Joseon

Chotdae, Candlestick
Joseon

Gyeongdae, Mirror Stand
Late Joseon

Hwajodo Byeongpung, **Folding Screen With Bird and Flower Drawings**

Late Joseon

Cotton-padded Clothing

Padded coats, hats and wristlets were part of Korean winter attire. Housewives spent a lot of time in the house padding the clothes with inner layers of cotton. They put special care in the clothing for their children, as the old saying goes 'a hundred stitches mean a hundred years in life'. Aside from their functionality traditional sewing tools, such as needles, thimbles and bars, were also objects of great beauty.

***Uiyang*, Record of Boy's Clothing Size**
19th century

***Nubi Jeogori*, Boy's Quilted Winter Jacket**
19th century

***Sombeoseon*, Cotton-Padded Socks**
20th century
Donated by Choi Jeong-deuk

Jobawi,
Women's Winter Hat
19th century

Nambawi,
Fur-Hemmed Hood
19th century
Donated by Choi Jun-ho

Baeja, Women's Vest
20th century
Donated by Lee Sang-gi

Baeja, Men's Vest
20th century

Ssia, Cotton Gin
20th century

Pobaekcheok, Ruler for Measuring Cloth

19-20th century

Nubige, Loop Pressing Bar

19th century

Silpae, Spool

19-20th century

Baneuljip, Needle Case

19-20th century

Gawi, Scissors

20th century

Banjitgori, Paper
Sewing Box

19th century

Sewing Folk Painting Property of The Korean Christian Museum, Soongsil University

Indupan, Ironing Board
Late Joseon

Indu, Iron with Small Head
19-20th century

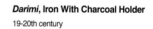

Darimi, Iron With Charcoal Holder
19-20th century

Hwaro, Brazier
Joseon

Ironing Folk Painting Property of The Korean Christian Museum, Soongsil University

Kitchen

Fireplace for cooking with an iron pot with chimney

Chanbang (Sub-Kitchen)

The *chanbang* was a small space usually located next to the kitchen, and had many uses. Primarily, it was a place where maids put cooked food on dishes before delivering them to the *sarangbang* and *anbang* on portable dining tables. Simple cooking was done in this room as well. The *chanbang* was also used to keep tableware, utensils, dining tables and rice chests.

Chanhap, Lunch Box
Late Joseon

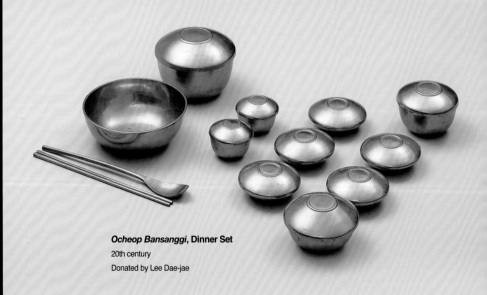

Ocheop Bansanggi, Dinner Set
20th century
Donated by Lee Dae-jae

Fermented Soybeans and Tofu

Meju or fermented soybeans, and tofu were made during the winter when food stuff was short. *Kimchi*, Korea's staple dish of fermented vegetables, was made sometime between late autumn and early winter. The preparation and making of *kimchi* is called *gimjang*.

Gyuhap Chongseo,
Encyclopedia for Women
19th century

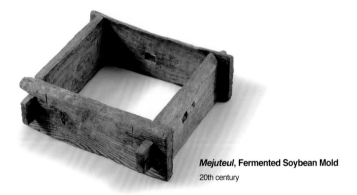

Hanguel Pyeonji, Letter from Daughter to Mother Written in Korean
20th century

Mejuteul, Fermented Soybean Mold
20th century

Maetdol, Hand Mill
20th century
Donated by Goh Jeong-hui

Dubuteul, Tofu Mold
20th century

Gimjang (Making of Kimchi)

During winter, Korean women gathered to collaborate on the laborious process of making enough *kimchi* for their families to last through the winter. The preparation and making of *kimchi* is called *gimjang*. *Kimchi* is clearly the most distinctive among the many traditional Korean pickled dishes and is made by pickling cabbages and other vegetables with salt and combining them with a variety of spices and condiments, before setting aside to ferment.

Kimchi was commonly buried underground in jars to be kept fresh. *Kimchi* was a crucial dish during the winter, when supplies of vegetables and other sources of nutrition were low. This explains why Koreans called the dish a 'winter staple'. Cabbage is the main ingredient of most *kimchi* today, but in the past, radishes, ground melons and other vegetables and fruits were more commonly used.

Bueokkal, Kitchen Knife
19th century

Doma, Cutting Board
20th century

**Banchandeungsok,
Recipe Book for Side
Dishes From Cheongju,
North Chungcheong
Province**
1913

**Yangnyeom Danji,
Condiment Jar**
19th century

Hwakdok, Mortar
20th century

jangdokdae, or jar stands, were used to secure the *onggi*, or earthenware jars, used as containers for condiments such as soy sauce, soybean paste, red-pepper paste and salted fish. The jar stand was usually found on the east side of the house to allow the vessels longer exposure to sunlight.

The *Jangdokdae* was also considered somewhat of a sacred place, thought of as a home to *Chilseong* the god that governs the fate of men, and *Cheolryung* the god responsible for the taste of fermented food. Family members often held rituals in front of the jar stand to honor *Chilseong* or hung gold-colored ropes on the jars to please *Cheolryung*. Thus, it was important for the women of the house to keep the jar stands clean and orderly at all times.

Onggi, a type of Korean clay pottery with dark-brown glaze, are often called as 'jars that breathe' and can be explained by the countless, micro-air holes on the surface of the vessels that allow air to circulate. This helps the condiments to taste fresh - and to last for years.

It was important to provide space between the jars on the *jangdokdae* for air circulation and to keep the jars from over-heating, which would lead the foods within to spoil.

Gorgan was a storeroom for threshed grain and seeds. The granary was distinguished by a big lock on its doors to discourage potential thieves.

Epilogue

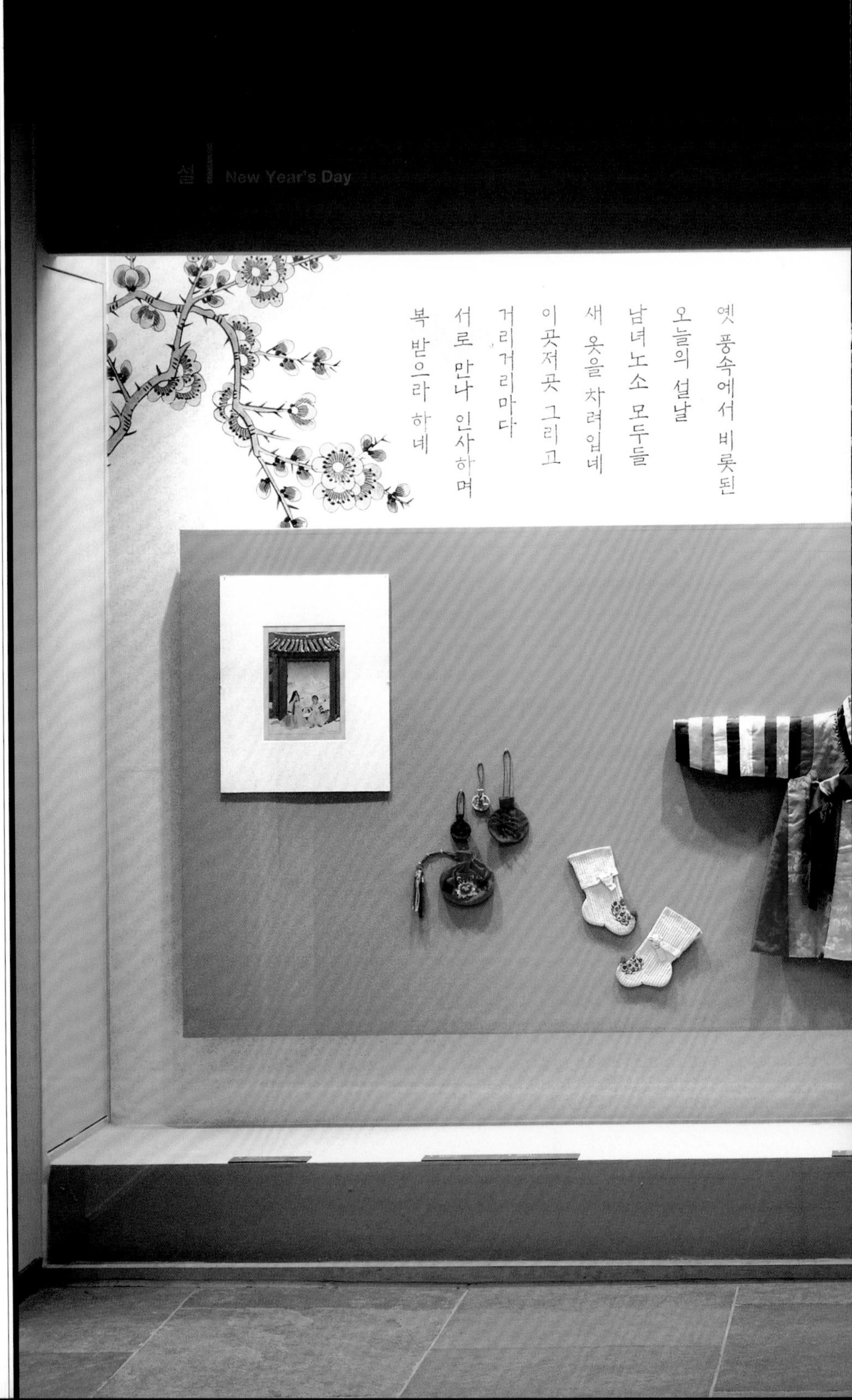
설
New Year's Day
옛 풍속에서 비롯된
오늘의 설날
남녀노소 모두들
새 옷을 차려입네
이곳저곳 그리고
거리거리마다
서로 만나 인사하며
복 받으라 하네

Lunar New Year's Day

Seollal (New Year's Day) is the first day of the lunar calendar. There are various traditional customs for *seollal* when family members bless each other and wish all good fortune for the New Year.

These customs include *seolbim*, *charye*, *sebae*, *deokdam* and *bokjorigeolgi*. *Bojagi* or wrapping cloth, were used to wrap food and other goods to be shared with relatives and neighbors.

It is hard to find a better symbol for Korean hospitality than bojagi, a product that exemplifies the simple beauty of Korean everyday life.

Kkachi Durumagi, Children's Five-Colored Coat for New Year's Day
20th century

Duru Jumeoni, Purse
19th century

Two Children 20th century Painting by Elizabeth Keith

Elizabeth Keith

Jeong (Loyalty, Love, Devotion)

Bojagi is a traditional wrapping cloth made from patching together scraps, which is then used to wrap goods enabling them to be carried.

There is not only a sense of practicality attached to wrapping, storing or carrying: *bojagi* also reflect the Korean traditional love of giving and forgiving, based on an unusually strong cultural sense of community.

Aside from their useful functions, *bojagi* also embody *jeong* - a word that describes the feeling of loyalty, love and devotion.

Wrapping Cloth
20th century

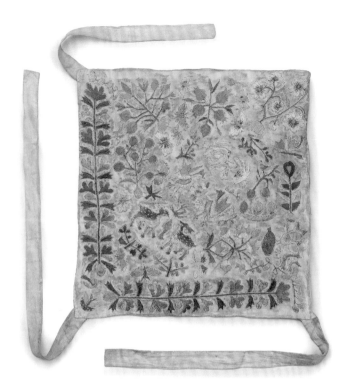

Wrapping Cloth for Wedding Goose

20th century

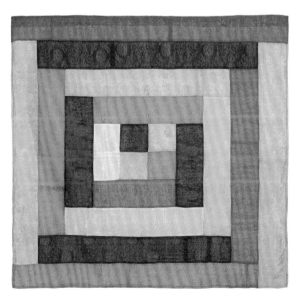

Wrapping Cloth

20th century

❶ Birth
❷ Education
❸ Coming of Age Ceremonies
❹ Marriage
❺ Family

❻ Success in the World
❼ Elegant Tastes
❽ Healing Disease
❾ The Sixtieth Birthday
❿ Mourning
⓫ Ancestral Rites

Here we introduce the major events in the life of an individual of the elite *Yangban* class of the Joseon Kingdom (1392-1910).

Joseon society placed a premium on the continuation of family lineage through male heirs. Boys were therefore universally preferred. The birth of a child, particularly a boy, and his healthy growth was celebrated on the 100th day after birth and on his first birthday. Boys and girls had different ceremonies for coming of age and they formed their own families through marriage.

Men first placed their foot on path to a successful career by passing the government public service entrance examinations, whereas women regarded keeping house as their primary obligation.

Sorrow over the death of a family member was observed and overcome during a three-year mourning period. The memorial tablets of ancestors were kept at a family shrine. Ancestral rites were held regularly to entreat ancestors for their benevolence in bringing prosperity and harmony to their descendants and the clan.

Korean Life Passages

All families wished for sons because, in Joseon society, the family line was continued through the son. Prayers were offered to the goddess of birth (*Samsin halmeoni*) to bless a family with as many sons as possible.

The birth of a child was announced by hanging a straw rope across the front gate of the house. Traditionally, the placenta was buried in a clean spot to ensure that the child would grow up well. In view of the high infant mortality in traditional society, circumspectly, the birth of a child was not formally celebrated until a feast was held on the 100th day after birth. A larger feast was given on the first birthday, at which the child's future was predicted.

The Bridal Room

The bride and the groom spent their wedding night in the bridal room (*Sinbang*) decorated with auspicious patterns symbolizing everlasting love and conjugal harmony: flowers, birds and butterflies. Traditionally, the bed sheets had colorful embroidered designs of happy pairs of mandarin duck. Bridal rooms usually had a folding screen again featuring designs of flowers and birds, or flowers and butterflies, and candlesticks further decorated with butterfly designs.

Key Holder

Late Joseon

Donated by Jeong Seong-chae

The *yeolsoepae*, or key holder, knots together several dowry charms brought by the bride at marriage. It was hung on furniture as symbols to wish the family peace and prosperity.

Axe-Shaped Pendant, Worn in Wish to Give Birth to a Son

Late Joseon

When a baby was expected, the family prayed to the Goddess of Birth (*Samsin*) to protect both baby and mother. Before birth, prayers were offered with a bowl of uncooked rice, a bunch of dried seaweed and a bowl of pure water placed on a special table (*Samsin-sang*) covered with clean mulberry paper.

Immediately after delivery, the rice on the table was cooked and the seaweed was made into soup for the mother to eat. Also, a table of special foods was offered to the goddess to seek her benevolence so that the baby would grow up well and free from any troubles.

**Table and Jar for
Goddess of Birth**
2006
Replica

Taboo Line
2006
Replica
Upon the birth of a child,
the *geumjul*, or straw
rope, was hung across
the gate, which was to
frighten away evil spirits
or ill-willed persons.

Taboo Line

When a baby was born a special straw rope, a *geumjul*, was hung across the gate of the house to announce the child s birth together with its gender. For a boy the rope was inserted with red peppers and charcoal. For a girl: charcoal and pine twigs. The rope was believed to drive away evil spirits as well as any impure visitors. It was removed from the gate after 21 days.

Placenta Chamber

The placenta of a newborn baby was carefully stored, as it was believed to contain the baby's vital energy. In the royal or noble households, a baby's placenta was sealed in a jar and placed within a special underground chamber (*Taesil*) in the mountains. An auspicious day was picked, by divination, for this task. Commoners covered a placenta with chaff and burned it or buried it in a clean area of earth.

Outer Container for Placenta Container
Late Joseon

Container for Placenta
Late Joseon

A feast was held on a child's first birthday (*Dol*) to celebrate a safe first year of life. The highlight of the celebration was a ritual foretelling the future of the child. For the ritual a special table was prepared with a variety of objects as well as white rice cakes and a bundle of threads: both symbolized long life. The object first picked by the child was believed to foretell its future: money or grain meant wealth: a book or writing brush, a scholar-official: an arrow or a bow, a general. When a girl picked up a spool or scissors, it was believed that she would be good at needlework.

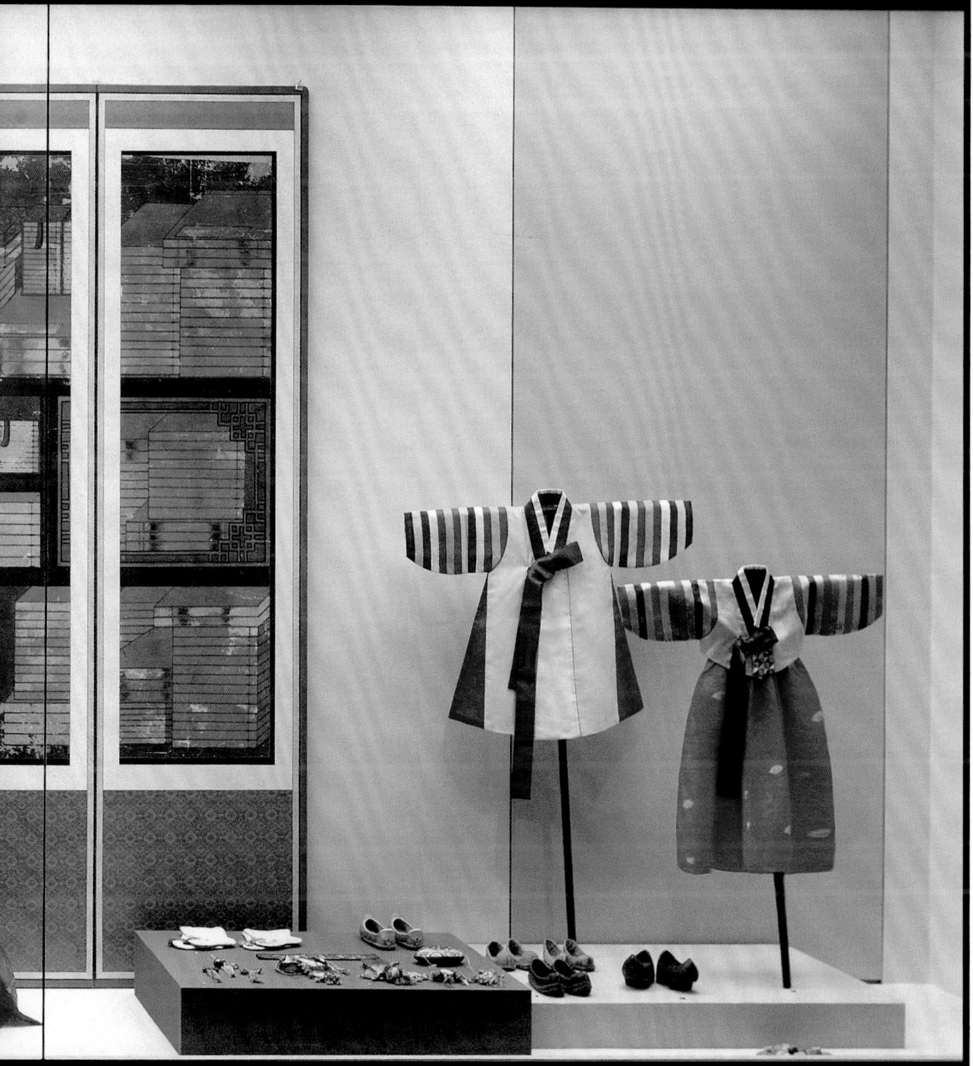

Boy's Five-colored Coat

Late Joseon

Girl's Rainbow Top

1991

Donated by Park Gwang-hoon

**Waist Band for Child's
First Birthday Coat**

Late Joseon

**Quilted Socks With
Embroidered Patterns**

1950s

**Meal Setting for
First Birthday**

度觀嬉

First Birthday Ritual Folk Painting 19th century

Education

Joseon society aimed at setting high moral standards through ethical education based on Confucian teachings about basic human relations. The government distributed illustrated ethical books translated into the native alphabet (*Hangeul*) and honored those who set outstanding examples as filial sons, loyal subjects or faithful wives.

Boys studied Chinese characters and ethics at private elementary schools (*Seodang*) and continued their education in character development and in preparation for the civil service examinations at local public schools (*Hyanggyo*) or private Confucian academies (*Seowon*). They studied classical Confucian texts, history books and astronomical charts. Women were taught ethics and the Korean alphabet at home. They acquired information and knowledge by exchanging correspondence or reading books translated into Korean.

Ethics

Confucianism defined differing duties for different status in human relations. The relationships between *ruler and subject, father and son, and husband and wife* were regarded as the three human bonds of supreme importance. To these were added the relations between the *senior and junior* and those *bonded by friendship*. These five constituted the basic moral principles, *Samgangoryun*.

The government of Joseon presented awards to those who set notable examples as filial sons, loyal subjects or faithful wives. It also undertook projects to distribute Korean versions of ethics textbooks, with illustrations, such as *Samganghaengsil-do* and *Oryunhaengsil-do*. The literati decorated their houses with folding screens featuring pictorial images or Chinese characters symbolizing important Confucian moral concepts.

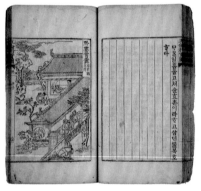

Oryunhaengsildo,
Illustrations on the Five Virtues
1797

Samganghaengsildo, Illustrations on the
Three Bonds
Late Joseon

Folding Screen with Letter Drawings

Late Joseon

A folding screen with animated Chinese characters describing the eight
important Confucian values.

Elementary School

Seodang were private elementary community schools for young children that flourished during the latter half of the Joseon dynasty. Boys from the age of six or seven entered these schools to read Chinese primers and Confucian classics adapted for children. They learned these books by heart and practiced writing with a brush.

Wooden Board for Practicing Calligraphy
Joseon

Bamboo Strip Holder
Late Joseon

Bookmark for Counting Memorized Paragraphs
Late Joseon

Education:
Astronomy and Geography

Koreans of the Joseon period believed that
the sun circled the earth, and that heaven
was round while the earth was square. They
studied astronomy with a celestial globe
(*Honcheoneui*) to understand the heavenly
bodies and their movements, and measured
time and the 24 seasons of the year by using
astronomical maps (*Cheonmundo*) and
sundials (*Haesigye*). They also learned
place names and famous historical and
scenic points around Joseon, and of its
place in the world, through China-centered
world maps.

Sundial
Late Joseon

Celestial Globe
Late Joseon
Property of Sun Gallery

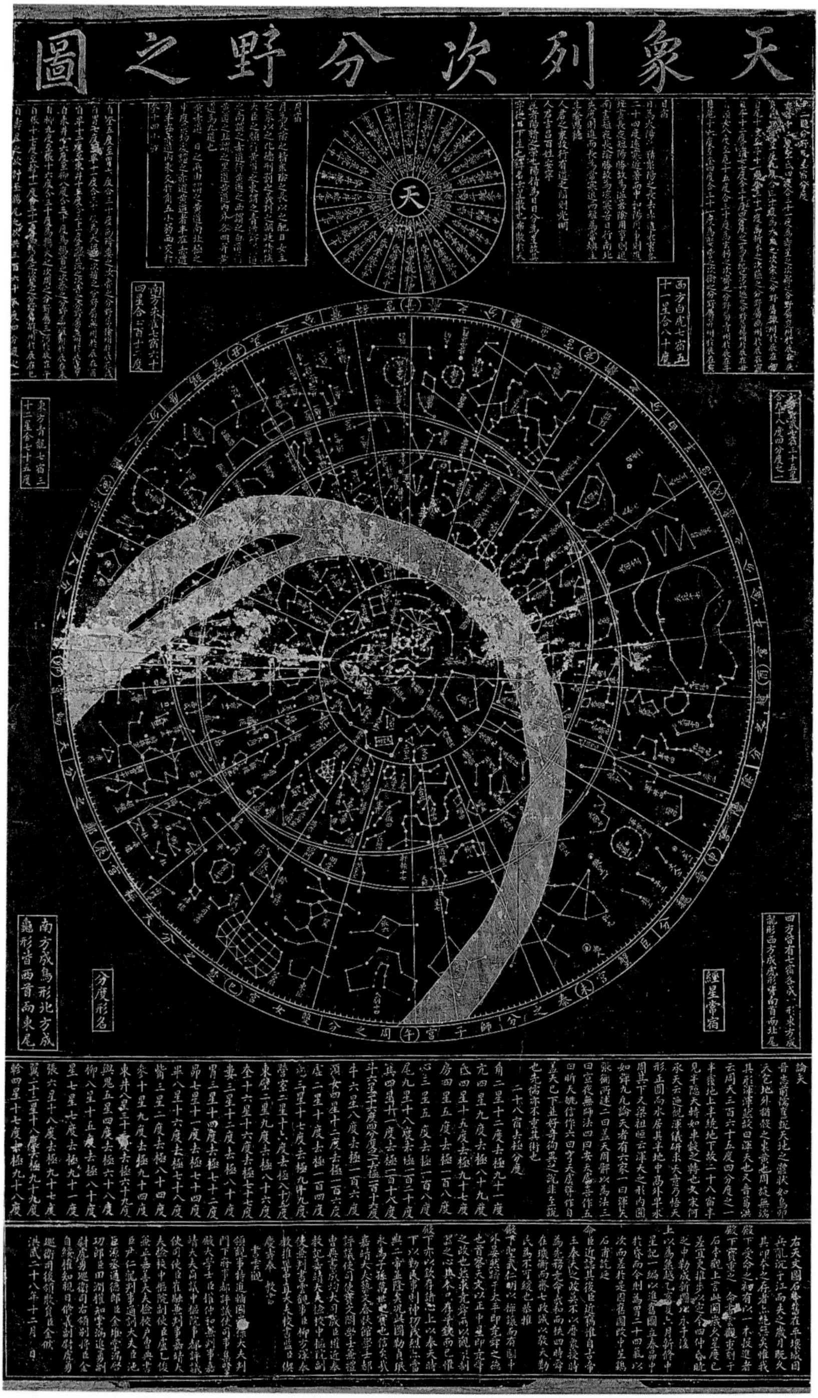

Rubbed Copy of Stone-engraved Star Chart

Late Joseon

Donated by Hwang Yong-ju, Hwang Min-hwan

Books for Study

Chinese characters were widely used during the Joseon dynasty. Young boys went to private elementary schools (*Seodang*) to learn their meanings and pronunciations with the help of a popular primer the 'Thousand Character Classic (*Chonjamun*)'. For basic moral education, they also read books on the 'Three Bonds and Five Cardinal Relationships (*Samgangoryun*)' and on prominent moral achievements by the ancient sages. Boys advanced to local public schools (*Hyanggyo*) or private Confucian academies (*Seowon*) to continue their studies in Chinese classics and history in preparation for the civil service examinations. They committed famous passages from Chinese classics to memory so as to improve their literary ability.

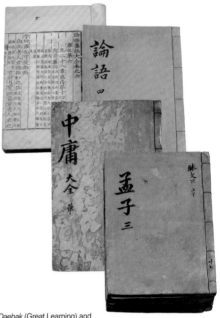

Classic Textbooks

Noeo (Analects of Confucius), *Daehak* (Great Learning) and *Jungyong* (Doctrine of the Mean) were among the representative books in Confucian learning.

Book Box

20th century

Stationery

Stationery items (*Munbanggu*) used for writing and reading, were indispensable utensils in schools as well as for private study. The Joseon literati, who highly respected academic learning, particularly regarded paper, writing brushes, ink and ink stones as the 'four friends of the scholar(*Munbangsau*)' that must always be kept nearby. They liked to decorate their studies with paintings featuring assorted stationary articles and ancient bronze ware considered to symbolize scholarly conviction and the pursuit of Confucian ideals.

Water Dropper
Late Joseon
A water-dropper was used to dilute the cake of ink on the ink stone for use in painting or calligraphy.

Ink Stick and Ink Stick Stand
Late Joseon

Ink Slab
Late Joseon

Ink Slab Case
Late Joseon

Brush Holder

Late Joseon

Writing Brush

Late Joseon

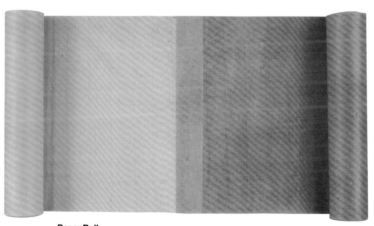

Paper Roll

Late Joseon

Coming of Age Ceremonies

Joseon men had a coming-of-age ceremony (*Gwallye*) around the time they reached their twentieth birthday. In the presence of elders, representing their clans, they went through elaborate procedures of tying their hair in a topknot (*Sangtu*) putting on a set of formal headgear, including a black hemp hat (*Chipogwan*), the Confucian student's cap (*Yugeon*) and a wide-brimmed black horsehair hat (*Gat*) - and receiving the name that would be used in their adulthood (*Ja*).

Women wore a chignon (*Jjok*) fixed with a long hairpin (*Binyeo*) for the first time for their coming-of-age ceremony (*Gyerye*), usually held around the age of 15. Significantly, for women, the wedding ceremony often replaced the coming-of-age ceremony.

Coming of Age Ceremony

Topknot Cover
19th century

Topknot Pin
Late Joseon

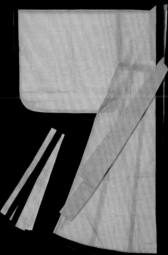

White Overcoat With Black Trims, Worn by Confucian Scholars
Late Joseon

Women's Ceremonial Hair Ornament
20th century

Long Hairpin
20th century

Ritual Garment for Noble Women
Late Joseon

In Joseon society, parents used a go-between to arrange marriages. When two families agreed to the marriage of their children, the bridegroom's family sent a letter of betrothal and a box of bridal gifts to the bride's family.

The wedding ceremony (*Hollye*) was usually held at the bride's home. On the wedding day, the groom came to the bride's house carrying a goose carved of wood to offer as a symbol of his everlasting fidelity. The bride and groom then exchanged bows and shared wine from a gourd cup.

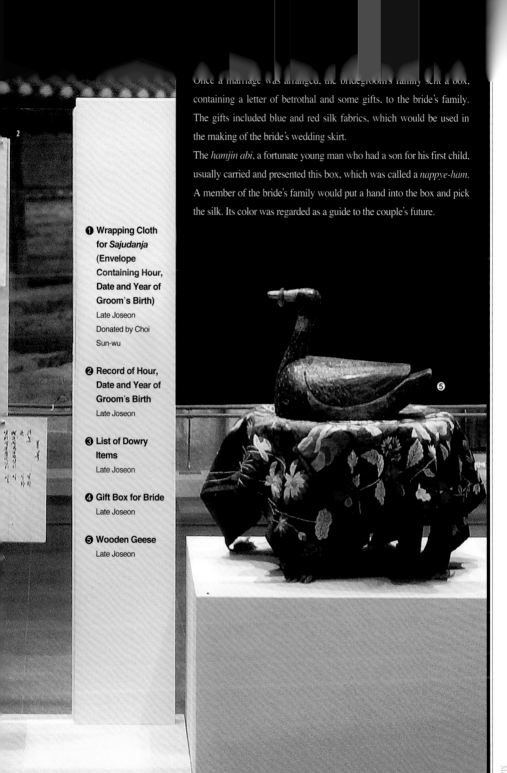

Once a marriage was arranged, the bridegroom's family sent a box, containing a letter of betrothal and some gifts, to the bride's family. The gifts included blue and red silk fabrics, which would be used in the making of the bride's wedding skirt.

The *hamjin abi*, a fortunate young man who had a son for his first child, usually carried and presented this box, which was called a *nappye-ham*. A member of the bride's family would put a hand into the box and pick the silk. Its color was regarded as a guide to the couple's future.

❶ Wrapping Cloth for *Sajudanja* (Envelope Containing Hour, Date and Year of Groom's Birth)
Late Joseon
Donated by Choi Sun-wu

❷ Record of Hour, Date and Year of Groom's Birth
Late Joseon

❸ List of Dowry Items
Late Joseon

❹ Gift Box for Bride
Late Joseon

❺ Wooden Geese
Late Joseon

The Wedding

It was customary for the bride and groom to meet for the first time at their wedding ceremony. In most regions across the country, the wedding ceremony was held at the bride's home, usually in the main hall (*Daecheong*) or in the yard (*Madang*), which were, for this period, both named *Chorye-cheong*, literally 'wedding hall'.

The officiator presided over the ceremony from behind the wedding table. The groom stood at the east and the bride at the west. The bride and groom exchanged deep bows and shared a cup of wine to complete the ceremony.

Women's Ceremonial Hair Ornament
20th century

Hwarot
Early 20th century
Donated by Son Gyeong-ja
Hwarot is a type Korean traditional clothing
worn by royal women for ceremonial
occasions or by commoners for weddings
during the Joseon Kingdom.

Wedding Hall(recreation)

Bride's Sedan Chiar

Late Joseon

After the wedding ceremony the bride went to the groom's house in a colorfully decorated sedan chiar carried by four men (*Sain-gyo*). A piece of tiger's skin or a tiger-patterned quilt was put on top of the sedan chiar to ward off misfortunes. Underneath the bride's cushion were put charcoal and cotton seeds, which respectively were believed to chase away bad luck and ensure fertility.

A Father's Writing for His Daughter on Her Marriage

- From A Father's Instructions for Daughter (*Gyenyeoseo*) by Song Si-yeol (pen name Uam, 1607-1689)

As you are getting married when you have yet to reach adulthood, I cannot keep you by my side to teach you until I grow old, and instead must send you away to another family. I feel heavy with concern and embarrassment that you may find yourself at a loss over etiquette or any other matter. Therefore, I am writing all my detailed opinions on various matters as a precaution. Please engrave these words into your heart and read this book a few times a month so that you will not forget.

Folding Screen with Peony Patterns

Early 20th century

A folding screen decorated with drawings of peony flowers, which symbolized
prosperity. It was used for ceremonies such as weddings or feasts.

Exhibited here are the family relics of the Hwang Clan of Changwon, donated by Hwang Yong-ju and Hwang Min-hwan. The items include the genealogical record of the family, a letter written by a father to his daughter ahead of her wedding, and a son's letter to his father inquiring about his health, all offering a glimpse of family life during the late Joseon period.

가계 계승 Succession of Family Lineage

Genealogical Table

Joseon society placed great importance on continuing family lineage through male heirs, which was considered the central element of family values. The bondage was strong between family members and relatives who shared the same ancestors. During the late Joseon Kindgom, families even adopted foster children to continue family lines. The *jokbo* is a Korean genealogical record equivalent to the family tree. Detailed information of an individual is recorded on the list, including name, name at birth and adult name, penname, posthumous name, former bureaucratic titles, authored books and documents, lifetime achievements, month and year of death and location of the grave.

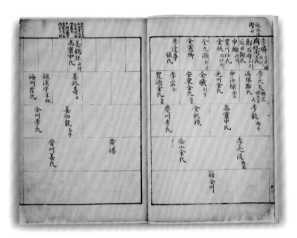

Family Tree
19th century
Donated by Hwang Yong-ju, Hwang Min-hwan

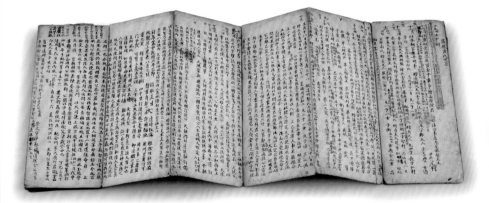

Pedigree of the Hwang Clan of Changwon
18th century
Donated by Hwang Yong-ju, Hwang Min-hwan

Portrait of Hwang Shin

Late Joseon

Donated by Hwang Yong-ju, Hwang Min-hwan

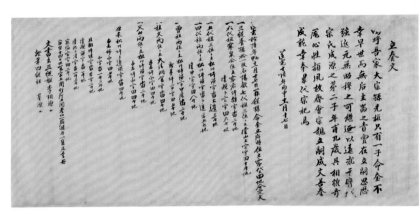

Certificate of Adoption

1836

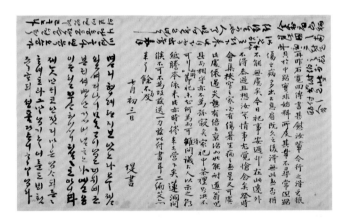

A Letter from Father to Son

By Hwang Ha-shin

Donated by Hwang Yong-ju, Hwang Min-hwan

Thank you for your letter, which Seok-gwan brought on his way back the day before yesterday. It is good to learn that you all have arrived safely. But I am still concerned that any illness that began on the way may appear later. How was the ancestral rite held today? I feel even sadder when I think of you all as I am far away and cannot be with you. Many people must have gathered at the time of the rite. I am concerned they might have suffered from heat in our small house. I am managing somehow to get along. It is hotter here than in Seoul, but with Ong-a by my side, I am not lonely because we can depend on each other.

The 3rd of July

From Gimje

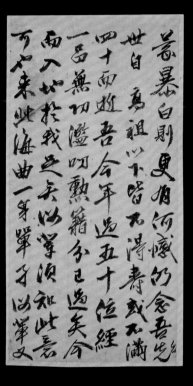
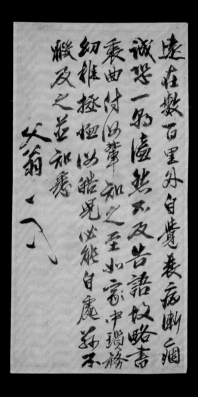

A Father's Will to His Children

By Hwang Shin

Donated by Hwang Yong-ju, Hwang Min-hwan

I came to this remote place by myself, and you are all hundreds of miles away. As I feel my illness is growing ever more serious at this old age, I am afraid that I may die all of a sudden one day before letting you know what I think. Therefore, I am writing briefly about my thoughts and hope that you will understand. If any complicated events befall our family, love the young ones and help those in need. I believe you, Il-ho, will handle everything well. I am writing hurriedly with the hope that everyone will properly understand me.

Drawings of Filial Piety

19th century

The folding screen is illustrated with *hyojado*, or paintings of famous stories about filial piety.

Red Spiked Gate

1883

With a view to enhancing moral standards among the public, the Joseon government honored those who set prominent examples as loyal subjects, filial sons or faithful wives by erecting red spiked gates near the entrance to their villages or houses. These gates were called "*Jeongnyeo*" or "*Hongsal-mun*." The gate exhibited here was set up in 1883 in honor of Jeong Se-ryang of Sancheong County, South Gyeongsang Province. Jeong was recommended for the honor by his neighbors in recognition of his great filial devotion, which was said to have moved the heavens to instruct a tiger to bring him deer meat to feed his ailing mother.

Hyojagak

Hyojagak were small buildings built to protect commemorative tablets honoring filial piety. The tablet exhibited here was dedicated to a person named Heo Kwon(1847-1895) and is distinctive for its structural beauty and sophisticated engraved patterns.

Though the Joseon period was exemplified by a rigid class structure, upward social mobility was legally possible for those who passed the civil service examinations (*Gwageo*). On occasion appointments to government posts were made due to the merits of an ancestor. However, joining officialdom by passing the state examinations was the surest way to a successful public career

for men in Joseon society, a society that respected academic accomplishment.

The Confucian-educated officials of the Joseon regarded righteousness and loyalty to their king as the most just course for a literati (*Sadaebu*). Therefore, they did not hesitate to give honest counsel to the king, even at the cost of their lives.

Civil Service Examinations

Legally, the civil service examinations (*Gwageo*) offered opportunity for all educated men to make their way into officialdom within the capital. Passing the examinations ensured appointment to a government post, which was both a most coveted path to success for the individual and a great honor for his family. Those who passed the civil and military examinations paraded, with a band, in a three-day visit to their relatives and proctors. On this exciting occasion, graduates would put special artificial flowers in their hats.

Civil Service Examination Papers

1885

Donated by Jang Yang-won

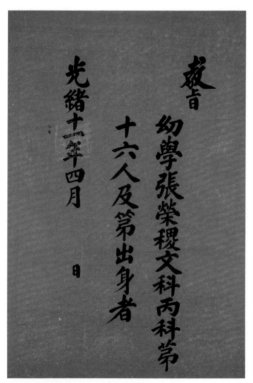

Certificate of Passing the Final Round of Civil Service Examinations

1885

Donated by Jang Yang-won

Flowers of Royal Inspector

Late Joseon

Three-Day Visit After Passing Exam Folk Painting 19th century

Civil Officials

Civil officials (*Mungwan*) were recruited through state examinations conducted at two levels: on knowledge in Confucian classics and skill in writing poetry, prose and essay.

In Joseon society, civil officials were given greater privileges than military officials since its culture leant toward a respected for academic learning. These officials were not only given rights in the personnel administration of the court but also the right to command in the military. Therefore, it was considered the greatest of successes and highly honorable to join the public service through the passing of the civil

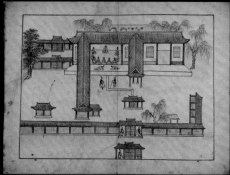

**Album of Fraternity Meeting
of Officials of the Office of
Inspector-General**
1813

Military Officials

Military officials (*Mugwan*) were recruited through the state examinations on knowledge in military texts and skills in military arts such as archery and horseback maneuvering.

While legally they ranked parallel with civil officials, in reality civil officials gained far better treatment because of the high respect academic learning commanded in Confucian-oriented Joseon society.

Military examinations were held every year and, despite obvious discrimination in status, the annual examinations expanded opportunities for those of lower class to rise socially. Candidates' required qualifications were eased markedly in the wake of the Japanese Hideyoshi invasions from 1592 to 1598.

Solider Identification Tag
Late Joseon
The tags were used by regional military authorities
when mobilizing soldiers.

Carrying Pouch for a Military ID tag
Late Joseon

**Ornamental Patches with Embroidered Designs Attached on the Front
and Back of Officials' Uniforms**
Late Joseon
Donated by Kim Hye-kyung

Official Wardrobes

Jobok and *jebok* were ceremonial robes worn by government officials during the Joseon Kingdom when they participated in memorial services for deceased kings and queens at the *Jongmyo* Shrine and *Sajik* Shrine. *Jebok* were equipped with ornaments such as *paeok*, or jade pendants, and *husu*, or back panels. As with the patterns of *hyungbae*, or embroidered patches on the breast and back of the official robes, the color of the jade pendants, which were either green or white, was an indicator of bureaucratic rank. The design of *husu* also differed by bureaucratic rank, including the colors, embroidered patterns and the ornamental knots attached to the panel. In the later days of the Joseon Kingdom, *paeok* and *husu* faded as status indicators and were merely considered as ornamental items.

Official's Ceremonial Crown

Joseon

Jade Ornamennts

Late Joseon

Jebok

20th century

Ceremonial robes worn by government officials during the Joseon Kingdom when they participated in rites at the *Jongmyo* Shrine and *Sajik* Shrine.

Ornamental Stick for a Public Official

Late Joseon

Sash

Late Joseon

A Sedan Chair for a High Official

Joseon officials of the senior second rank (*Jeong i-pum*), or higher, used a special sedan chair called a *Choheon*, which had a single wheel and long side-poles. More than five men pulled these sedan chairs. Officials who used them lived in houses with a high gate (*Soseul daemun*) without a threshold so that the cart-like, high-riding sedan chairs could more easily pass through.

Sedan Chair for High Official
Late Joseon

權縮符

March of Government Official Folk Painting 19th century

Cheoninsan

During the Joseon period, residents might present a sun parasol (*Cheoninsan*) to their local official as a tribute to his achievements and hard work, with all the residents' names embroidered on its canopy.

This parasol had two different names - *cheoninsan* and *maninsan* - depending on the number of those participating in its presentation. In Eastern cultures, the characters for *cheon* means thousands, *man* millions, but they both broadly denote a very large number. So, *cheoninsan* would indicate a parasol presented by a large number of the residents of a village to a single official.

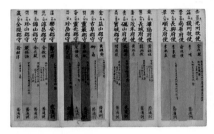

Roster of Magistrates in Jeolla Province
1856

Cheoninsan
1885

Government Official Under Sunshade Folk Painting Early 20th century

Joseon aristocrats placed great value on enjoying the peace of nature as a break from their daily routine. Amidst nature's beauties, they enjoyed drinking and listening to music, either played on the popular zither, *Geomungo*, or in *Pansori* - narrative folk songs. The *yangban* also composed rhyming poetry or contemplated paintings.

These were all regarded as important activities for cultivating those elegant artistic tastes (*Pungnyu*) suited to all educated elite.

Some also enjoyed playing *baduk* (go) or *janggi* (chess) while others trained mind and body through archery or games of *tuho* (throwing arrows into a jar).

Recreation

The nobles of the Joseon dynasty sought relief from intellectual rigor by indulging in various forms of entertainment and recreation.

With family or friends, in the *sarangbang*, or in the outdoors, they enjoyed games such as *baduk*, *janggi* or *tuho* with. In the mountains or fields, they trained their body through archery.

Additionally, aristocrats cultivated virtue and concentration through *tuho* and archery, as each pursuit required great focus and control. Each village promoted solidarity and unity amongst their inhabitants through these recreational activities.

Tuho, Throwing Arrow Game
Late Joseon

Double Six Game
1900s

Ssangryuk, Dice Game
Painting by Kim Jun-geun
20th century

Janggi, Chess
Late Joseon

Baduk, Go
Late Joseon

Archery

Archery (*Hwal-ssogi*) has been a popular sport among Koreans since ancient times. The learned elite of Joseon, the literati, considered it to be an important martial art that they must acquire and practice. They believed the sport not only good for physical and mental discipline but also for the cultivation of a person's virtuous character.

The skill of the bowman was tested both on hunting excursions and when villages held archery contests for the young literati that aided both friendship and harmony.

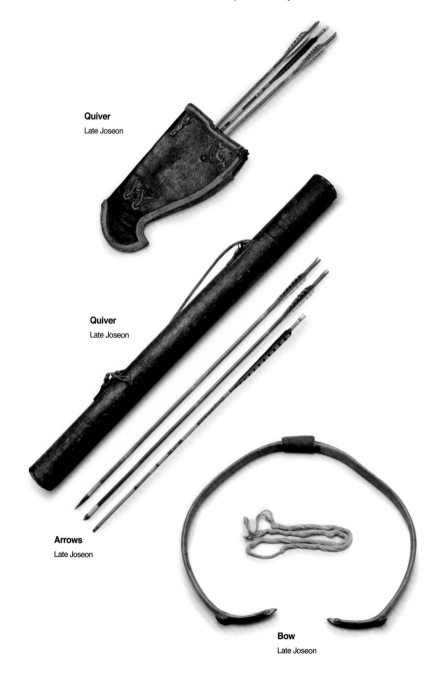

Quiver
Late Joseon

Quiver
Late Joseon

Arrows
Late Joseon

Bow
Late Joseon

Scholar Leaving for Archery Folk Painting Early 20th century

Sound

Similar to the tradition in other Asian countries, Koreans thought of music as more than just an art of sound, but as a metaphysical concept connected deeply with morality and ethics. This is evident in the philosophy of *yeak*, which is the underlying principle of court ritual music that pursues to perfection of tone and acoustic space. *Yeak* is a combination of two words, *ye*, which means rites, and *ak*, music. For Confucian scholars, an interest in *yeak* was regarded as a symbol of sophistication and important element in building one's character. So learning how to play the *geomungo*, a traditional string instrument similar to the zither, as well as other musical instruments, was considered a requirement. The noblemen were also skilled traditionally lyrical songs such as *sijo* and *gagok*.

Commoners had their own types of music to enjoy, most particularly *pungmul*, a folk music tradition that includes drumming, dancing and singing. *Pungmul* performances were often cited during dure, the collective laboring operations within farming communities, when farmer bands pounded on *kkwaenggwari* (small handheld gong), *janggu* (hourglass drum), *buk* (barrel drum) and *jing* (gong) to keep their spirits up.

Janggu, Drum
Late Joseon

Haegum, 2-string Pike Fiddle
Late Joseon

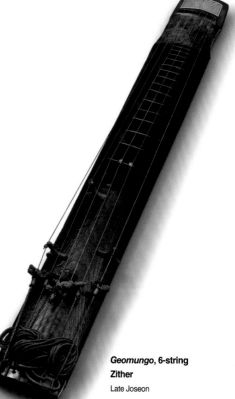

Geomungo, 6-string Zither
Late Joseon

Performing _Geomungo_ Folk painting· Early 20th century

Calligraphy and Painting

The Joseon literati considered it their greatest success in life to join public service through cultivation of their academic abilities. They also believed that a cultured gentleman must excel in all of the three arts: *Shi* (poetry), *Seo* (calligraphy) and *Hwa* (painting).

They enjoyed outdoor meetings at scenic locations where they composed poems or painted the landscape while appreciating one another's skills. They made albums of the paintings and calligraphic works produced to commemorate such meetings.

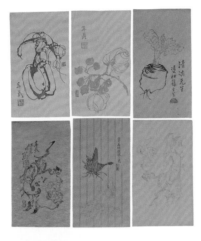

Letter Paper
Late Joseon

Wooden Printing Block for Letter Paper
Late Joseon

Paper Roll
Late Joseon

Scholars Making Poems and Drawing Paintings 18th century Individually Owned

Drawings of Stationery Items

19th century

Drawings of books, stationery items and antiques were popular during the
Joseon Kingdom, a reflection of the cultural taste of scholars.

Healing Disease

During the Joseon period, those who were sick, or in delicate health, saw herbalist doctors. With distribution of the landmark medical book, *Dong-eui bogam* (An Exemplar of Korean Medicine) - compiled by Heo Jun in 1610 - acupuncture and moxibustion (warming or burning with mugwort) came to be widely applied along with herbal medicines.

When these therapies did not work, people resorted to supernatural powers and, in seeking to cure or prevent disease, shamans were invited to perform exorcism or to prescribe talismans.

Traditional Chinese medical theory holds that pain or illness is caused by a loss of homeostasis between the 'five viscera and six organs (*Ojang yukbu*)'. In order to remedy an ailment, the blockage of vital energy (*gi*) or blood (*hyeol*) is released by opening the appropriate meridian (*gyeongnak*) or acupuncture point (*kyeonghyeol*).

The major sensitive points - 365 in all - and the paths connecting these points - the 14 meridians - are indicated in these anatomical charts and models.

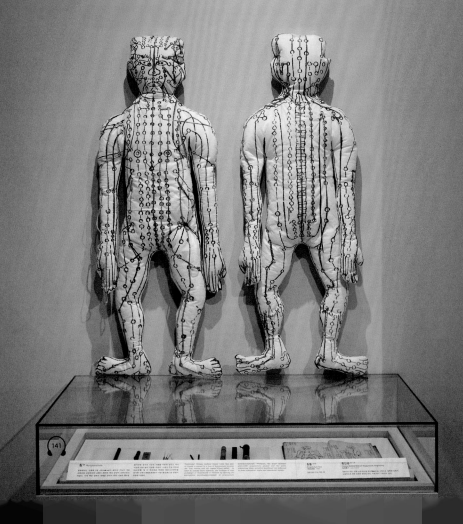

Korean Medicine Clinic

Traditional Korean medicine clinics (*Hanyak-bang*) provided healing services with a combination of pharmacology, acupuncture and moxibustion. Adoption of the *Dong-eui bogam*, based on ancient Korean and Chinese treatises, initiated epochal progress in Korean medical science.

Many clinics applied the new local theory dividing the constitution of human body into four different types. Here we can see an assistant cutting the necessary materials for a medicine.

Divination and Fortunetelling

Divination (*Jusul*) is the practice of attaining a certain goal with help from supernal powers. It was often performed as a seasonal custom, but more frequently for the purpose of preventing or curing disease with a reliance upon the ability of shamans to communicate with the supernatural world. Talismans were also used to expel evil spirits or misfortune. Fortunetelling (*Jeombok*) was also widely practiced.

**Printing Blocks
for Talismans**
Late Joseon

Talisman
Late Joseon

Printing Blocks for Talismans
Late Joseon

Illustrated Book on Fortunetelling

1943

Fortunetelling Tools

Early 20th century

Exorcism for Curing Smallpox

Smallpox and measles were among the most dreaded illnesses during the Joseon period: there were no remedies for either. Shamans were often invited to perform rites to appease the spirits governing these fatal diseases in the hopes of prevention or cure. These rites were called *byeolsang-gut* or *hogu-gut*. Reconstructed here is a *hogu-gut*: a female shaman conducts this particular rite - in her hands, a folding fan and set of rattles.

❶ Trident (Three-Pronged Spear)
After Liberation
Spear used by shamans in rituals.

❷ Shaman's Sword
After Liberation

❸ Shamanic Ritual Hat
After Liberation

❹ Shaman's Ritual Bells
1950s
Donated by Yang Jong-seung, Wu Myeong-dal

❺ Shaman's Sword
1950s

❻ Fodder-Chopper
1950s
Donated by Yang Jong-seung, Wu Myeong-dal

7 The Bell of the Great Dipper
Late Joseon

8 Five-Colored Flags Used in Shamanist Ritual
20th century

Flag used by shamans during rituals. The flag was marked in five colors - blue, white, red, black and yellow - which represented five directions.

9 Shaman's Mirror
1950s

Donated by Yang Jong-seung, Wu Myeong-dal

10 11 Portrait of Shamanist Deity
1900s

The portrait, which describes Byeolsang, a shamanist deity related to happiness and longevity, and Hogubuin, believed to control measles, was used in rituals to prevent smallpox.

12 Shamanic Ritual Fan
1950s

13 Rope of Shaman's Genealogy
1950s

At a period in history when few people lived into old age, the 60th birthday was considered especially important, since it marked the completion of a full cycle of the zodiac.

It was customary for children to celebrate a parent's 60th birthday (*Hwangap or Hoegap*) with a large feast and merrymaking. Many relatives and friends were invited to extend congratulations to the 60-year-old parent. As an expression of their filial affection and gratitude, the children prepared a special table laden with piles of colorful fruits and delicacies, and often decorated with

Different to the table for ancestral rites, the husband sat to the east and the wife to the west at the 60th-birthday table (*Hoegap-sang*). They received wine and obeisance from their spouse, their children, grandchildren and all their relatives (in order of age) with wishes of health and further longevity. The tradition remains, and is alive and well today.

When a parent died, the children considered it their duty to observe a three-year mourning period (*Samnyeon-sang*) as prescribed by the Confucian ethical code.

The funeral procession featured a colorful bier, and some human figurines and everyday objects were buried in the tomb to accompany the deceased into the next life. Throughout the mourning period, meals were offered at the family altar every morning and evening. Some might live in a grass hut, built near the parent's grave, during this time.

Bier

The biers (*Sang-yeo*) used for conveying the corpse to the burial site resembled palanquins, having long poles on both sides intended to be shouldered by 12 to 24 pallbearers. Most villages had such a bier for common use. It was designed to be disassembled for storage in a house removed a short distance from the neighborhood.

Bier
1856
Important Folklore Material No. 230
Donated by Jinju Hwadan Chinmokhoe

Funeral ode
1561

Moving of Bier 1961 Donated by Kim Eon-seok

Bier
1856
Important Folklore Material No. 230
Donated by Jinju Hwadan Chinmokhoe

Feng Shui : Determining Grave Sites

The ancient Taoist principles of *feng shui* were consulted in finding sites for the houses of the living (*Yangtaek*) as well as the houses for the dead (*Eumtaek*). Significantly, graves on propitious sites were believed to harness beneficial energy from their surroundings to bless the buried one's descendants. In the late Joseon period, the Confucian-oriented ruling elite criticized the negative consequences of this time-honored practice. Nonetheless, many moved the tombs of their ancestors or delayed funerals to look for propitious burial sites. Such efforts were considered commendable for correct ancestral worship.

Geomancer's Compass

Late Joseon

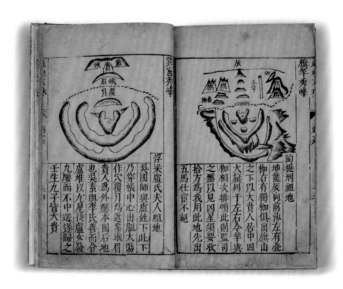

***Feng Shui* Guidebook**

Late Joseon

Wood Block for a Map of King Gyeongsun's Grave

Late Joseon

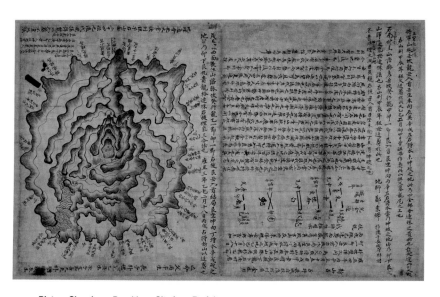

Picture Showing a Propitious Site for a Burial

1726

Memorial Stones

The personal information of the deceased, as well as the location of his or her grave, were recorded on a piece of stone or pottery and buried near the grave. These memorial stones (*Jiseok*) have been used since the Three Kingdoms period (57 BC-AD 668). Probably due to difficulties in obtaining proper stone, terracotta plates or ceramic bowls were also often used. The inscriptions grew shorter in later years, simply giving the name and official rank of the buried person.

Wooden Burial Figurines
1500s

Vessels for Burial Gifts
16-17th century

**Memorial Stone of
Jangsu hwangssi**

Late Joseon
Donated by Lee Gyu-seok

Memorial Stone of Jeong Dong-jun
1816

Memorial Stone of Jang Mun-gyu
1850

Shroud

Funeral procedures included washing the dead body and wrapping it with a shroud (*Su-eui*). A ceremonial outfit of the deceased was used in many cases, but no less frequently a special garment was made. As there was an old saying that 'a burial outfit prepared in advance brings longevity', many people made such garments for their parents as they approached the age of 60. They were made mostly during an intercalary month to ward off bad luck and long-lived women were invited to help.

Garments for the Dead
20th century

Garments for the Dead

20th century

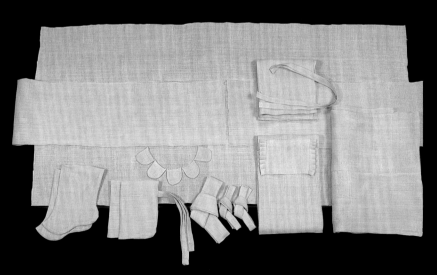

Garments for the Dead

20th century

Three-year Mourning Period

It was customary for children to offer meals to the spirit of their deceased parent every morning and evening for three years after the funeral. The meals were offered before the memorial tablet (*Sinju*) seated on a small wooden chair (*Yeongjwa*), which in turn was placed on an altar (*Sangcheong*). The children wore mourning clothes and refrained from any merriment during this period. After completion of the formal mourning period, they continued to hold memorial rites throughout their lives in order to fulfill their filial duties.

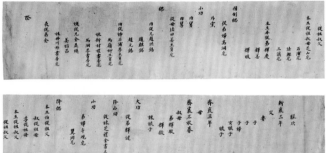

Bokchado

1910s

These documents clearly set forth the type of funeral garments mourners wear determined by how close a relationship they had to the deceased. This document was clearly posted on the funeral home during the funeral.

Book on Funeral Rituals

Late Joseon

The book describes the courses of rituals for funerals, from the period of mourning to the funeral service, as well as advisory for writing eulogies and passages on grave stones.

Stone Statues of Civil Officials That Once Stood in Front of a Tomb

16-17th century

Filial piety was practiced not only for living parents but ancestors as well. Solemn rites were performed to pay respects to ancestors, of up to four generations, on the eve of their death anniversaries and on holidays such as New Year's Day and the *Chuseok* harvest festival. Memorial tablets of these ancestors were kept at the family shrine (*Sadang*) for the rites

(Jesa), through which the ancestors had communion with their descendants. Those who did not have family shrines placed the memorial tablets in an alcove in the house or performed the rites before a picture of an ancestral shrine.

❶ **Frame for a Written Prayer**
Late Joseon

❷ **Incense Table**
Late Joseon

Incense Burner
1930s

Incense Box
1930s

❸ **Picture of Ancestral Shrine**
Late Joseon

❹ **Detailed Record of the Entire Procedures of**

❺ **List of the Dates for Ancestral Rites**
Late Joseon

❻ **Wooden Stand for Paper Memorial Tablets**
20th century

High Chair for Ancestral Tablet

❼ **Drawing of the Proper Arrangement of Food for Ancestral Rites**
1900s

Ritual Table

❽ **Spirit-Tablet Shrine**
Late Joseon

Picture of Ancestral Shrine
Late Joseon
Ancestral rites were sometimes held before a
picture of an ancestral shrine when there was no
family shrine or paper tablets had to be used for
rites observed away from home.

Vessels for Ancestral Rites

Bronze or porcelain vessels were used for ancestral rites held at the family shrine. Wooden ones were used for rites at the graveyard because they were easier to carry. The ritual vessels (*Jegi*), considered sacred, were kept in a special wooden chest. Nobody lent or sold these vessels to others. When they became unusable, they were buried for they were not to be used for any other purpose.

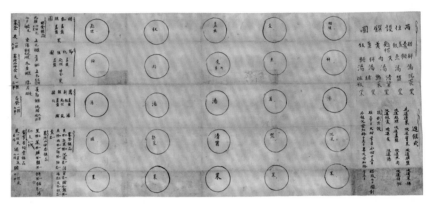

Drawing of the Proper Arrangement of Food for Ancestral Rites

1900s

Utensils Used for Ancestral Rites

20th century

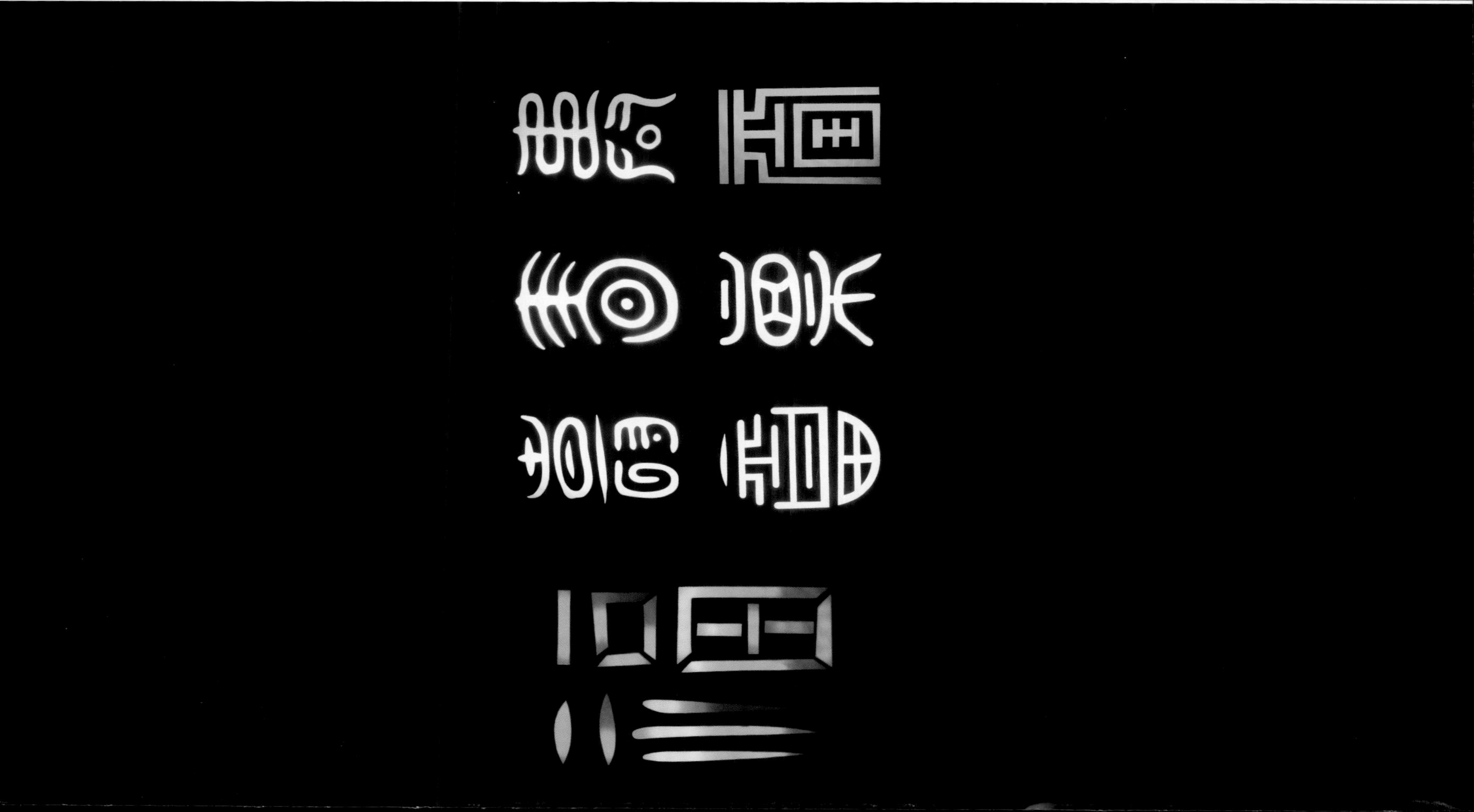

A Street to the Past: Experiencing Childhood

祝婚

草原의 빛

원리암 워지워지

여기에전인 이먹빛—
히미해주록
당신의 사랑하는 마음
당신의 ... 이 먹빛이
희미해잡다면 나는 당신을
...하는 날 ...
...을수 있겠습니다
...의 빛이여
...인의
...에 영광이여
...그것이 암토눌러 진다해도

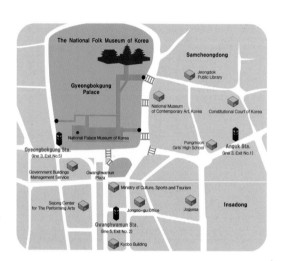

The National Folk Museum of Korea

Samcheongdong

Jeongdok
Public Library

Gyeongbokgung
Palace

National Museum
of Contemporary Art, Korea   Constitutional Court of Korea

National Palace Museum of Korea

Gyeongbokgung Sta.
(line 3, Exit No.5)

Pungmoon
Girls' High School   Anguk Sta.
(line 3, Exit No.1)

Government Buildings
Management Service   Gwanghwamun
Plaza

Ministry of Culture, Sports and Tourism

Sejong Center
for The Performing Arts   Jongno-gu Office   Jogyesa   Insadong

Gwanghwamun Sta.
(line 5, Exit No. 2)

Kyobo Building

First Printed	Sept. 20, 2009
First Published	Sept. 30, 2009

Compiled and Edited	The National Folk Museum of Korea
Planning and layout	The National Folk Museum of Korea
Editorial Director	Shin Kwang-seop
Executive Editors	Lee Kwan-ho, Kim Yoon-jeong, Lee Ju-young, Ji Hee-seung
Photographer	Seo Heun-kang
Translator	Kim Tong-hyung
Copy Editor	Suzanna Samstag Oh

Publisher	Tenmoon
Design	Tenmoon
Printing	Samwha Printing

Distributor	Tenmoon
Address	520-8, Munbal-li, Paju-si, Gyeonggi-do, Korea
Phone number	82-31-955-0075

국립민속박물관

National Folk
Museum of Korea

ISBN no.   **978-89-93684-16-2   03900**